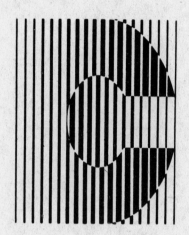

Student's Book

SPELLING MASTERY

a direct instruction series

Level C

Robert Dixon
Siegfried Engelmann

SCIENCE RESEARCH ASSOCIATES, INC.
Chicago, Henley-on-Thames, Sydney, Toronto

A Subsidiary of IBM

Printed in the United States of America

ISBN 0-574-72134-7

Lesson 1

Part A

green   keep   need   see   street   beetle   weed

Part B

I thought he was through.

_____

Part C

1. _ r i e _ _ _ _   4. _ _ _ i e _

2. _ _ o u g h   5. _ _ s t _ _

3. _ o _ _ e _

Part D

1. book •   • _ _ _ _ _ _
2. look •   • _ _ _ _ d
3. good •   • b _ _ _ _
4. stood •   • t _ _ _ _
5. took •   • _ _ _ _ _

Part E

These words are in the puzzle.
Circle 7 or more of the words.

beetle	friends	need
enough	blue	shut
should	talk	put
high	home	have

```
e b h t a l k
s n e e d e e
f r i e n d s
s s h n t b n
h s h o u l d
o i p u t u e
m n g g t e e
e s h h a v e
```

Lesson 2

Part A

1. _____
2. _____
3. _____
4. _____
5. _____

6. _____
7. _____
8. _____
9. _____
10. _____

Part B

1. __ h e __ __
2. __ o u __ __
3. __ __ __ l e
4. __ __ __ e __
5. __ a __ __

Part C

__ __ __ o u g h __   __ __   __ a __   __ __ __ o u g h .

_____

Part D

Figure out the words in the second column and write them.
Then draw lines to the same words in the first column.

1. come •   • __ __ n __
2. shove •   • __ __ __ __
3. none •   • d __ __ __
4. done •   • c __ __ __
5. some •   • __ __ m __
6. love •   • __ __ __ __ __

Part E

These words are in the puzzle.
Circle 7 or more of the words.

wonder	thought	listen
enough	stood	south
over	even	take
dog	wood	could

```
t a k e s c l
t h w n t o i
s t o o d u s
o e n u o l t
u v d g g d e
t e e h e h n
h n r r n o t
```

Lesson 3

Part A

-ack   -eck   -ick   -ock   -uck

Part B

_____ did you _____ Sandy?

Part C

__ ____ o u ____ __ ___ _____ g h.

Part D

I thout she was dunn.

Meny books are good.

Part E

Figure out the words in the second column and write them.
Then draw lines to the same words in the first column.

1. little   •   • _ _ _ _ u l _

2. were   •   • _ _ t t _ _

3. better   •   • _ _ o _ _ _

4. should   •   • _ _ _ _ _ e _

5. shove   •   • _ _ _ _ _

Part F

These words are in the puzzle.
Circle 7 or more of the words.

through   race   help
could   street   gone
oats   nose   should
cell   where   reach

```
s w h e r e s
t h r o u g h
r c e a t o o
e e o l c n u
e l a u p e l
t l t c l e d
n o s e h d d
```

Lesson 4

Part A

-ack   -eck   -ick   -ock   -uck

Part B

1. _____   4. _____

2. _____   5. _____

3. _____   6. _____

Part C

_____

Part D

1. _____   6. _____
2. _____   7. _____
3. _____   8. _____
4. _____   9. _____
5. _____   10. _____

Part E

Cross out the misspelled words in these sentences.
Then write the words correctly above the crossed-out words.

I think she is throo.

Do you have enuf frends?

Part F

Write each of these words in a box.

| would | green | thought | better | were | scold | should | book |
| south | good | over | little | many | where | listen | meet |

Lesson 5

Part A

-ack   -eck   -ick   -ock   -uck

Part B

I believe he lost every race.

_____

Part C

1. __ r u __ __

2. s __ __ l

3. __ o __ __

4. __ __ l __

5. __ o __ __ e __

Part D

I want you to _____ my _____ .

Part E

Cross out the misspelled words in these sentences.
Then write the words correctly above the crossed-out words.

I feel a litle bettor.

Your hoam is very quiut.

Part F

These words are in the puzzle.
Circle 7 or more of the words.

told	talks	better
able	after	above
vote	feel	anybody
neat	lie	light

```
a t a l k s a
a n n f i f a
b b e t t e r
o t l a o e e
v o t e t l r
e l i g h t d
a n y b o d y
```

Lesson 6

Part A

1. p<u>ack</u>   3. l<u>uck</u>   5. l<u>ock</u>   7. b<u>ack</u>   9. st<u>ack</u>

2. k<u>ick</u>   4. n<u>eck</u>   6. s<u>ick</u>   8. r<u>ock</u>   10. th<u>ick</u>

Part B

__ __e__i e___ ___ __o___ __e__y ___c e.

_____

Part C

1. _____   5. _____

2. _____   6. _____

3. _____   7. _____

4. _____   8. _____

Part D

I _____ like to _____ your brother.

Part E

Figure out each word and write it in the blank below.

erewh   ghouthr   woernd   iequt

1. _____ 2. _____ 3. _____ 4. _____

Part F

Figure out the words in the second column and write them.
Then draw lines to the same words in the first column.

1. neck   •   • __ __ __ c __

2. these •   • __ e __ __

3. then   •   • __ __ __ k

4. pack   •   • w __ __ __

5. thick •   • __ __ e __

6. want   •   • __ h __ __

Lesson 7

Part A

1. _____   5. _____

2. _____   6. _____

3. _____   7. _____

4. _____   8. _____

Part B

__ __ __ __ i e __ __ __ __ __ __ __ __ __ __ e __ y __ __ __ c __ .

_____

Part C

Figure out each word and write it in the blank below.

       namy   ckpa   iendfr   verye

1. _____ 2. _____ 3. _____ 4. _____

Part D

Cross out the misspelled words in these sentences.
Then write the words correctly above the crossed-out words.

I beleeve they are thru.

Do you think this is enogh?

Part E

Figure out the words in the second column and write them.
Then draw lines to the same words in the first column.

1. kick   •   • __ __ __ __ __ __

2. than   •   • __ i __ __

3. where   •   • __ __ __ e __

4. sack   •   • h __ __ __

5. little   •   • a __ __

6. wonder   •   • __ __ __ __ __ __

Lesson 8

Part A

     -adge   -edge   -idge   -odge   -udge

Part B

1. _____   4. _____

2. _____   5. _____

3. _____   6. _____

Part C

Did you _____ the dog _____ bark?

Part D

1. _____

2. _____

Part E

1. _____   5. _____

2. _____   6. _____

3. _____   7. _____

4. _____   8. _____

Part F

little   enough   wonder   listen   done   through

friends   home   where   every   street   thought

Part G

Figure out each word and write it in the blank below.

    kooc   cera   doulw   erbett

1. _____ 2. _____ 3. _____ 4. _____

Lesson 9

Part A

-adge   -edge   -idge   -odge   -udge

Part B

1. _____   5. _____
2. _____   6. _____
3. _____   7. _____
4. _____   8. _____

Part C

People watched from the other building.

_____

Part D

I _____ like some _____, please.

Part E

1. __ __ __ i __ __ __   4. __ __ e __ __
2. __ __ __ u __ __   5. __ __ a __ __
3. __ o __ __ __

Part F

stood   meet   enough   should   many   every

race   street   friends   quiet   through   wonder

Part G

Figure out each word and write it in the blank below.

peolpe   inkth   aylp   ownbr

1. _____ 2. _____ 3. _____ 4. _____

Lesson 10

Part A

-adge   -edge   -idge   -odge   -udge

Part B

1. _____   4. _____

2. _____   5. _____

3. _____   6. _____

Part C

__ e o __ l e __ __ a t c h __ __ __ __ o __ __ __ __

o __ __ e __ __ u i l __ __ __ __ .

_____

Part D

1. _____

2. _____

Part E

1. _____   10. _____

2. _____   11. _____

3. _____   12. _____

4. _____   13. _____

5. _____   14. _____

6. _____   15. _____

7. _____   16. _____

8. _____   17. _____

9. _____   18. _____

12

Part F

Figure out the words in the second column and write them.
Then draw lines to the same words in the first column.

1. blue •   • _ _ _ _ _

2. beetle •   • _ _ r _

3. port •   • _ o _ _

4. shock •   • _ _ _ _ _ _.

5. some •   • _ _ e _ _

6. these •   • _ _ _ _ k

Lesson 11

Part A

1. _____ 5. _____

2. _____ 6. _____

3. _____ 7. _____

4. _____ 8. _____

Part B

_ _ o _ _ _ _ _ _ t _ _ _ _ _ _ o _ _ _ _

o _ _ _ _ _ u i _ _ _ _ _.

Part C

1. b<u>a</u><u>dge</u>   4. <u>j</u><u>udge</u>   7. h<u>e</u><u>dge</u>

2. br<u>i</u><u>dge</u>   5. <u>ledge</u>   8. ri<u>dge</u>

3. d<u>o</u><u>dge</u>   6. f<u>udge</u>   9. pl<u>edge</u>

Part D

1. _____

2. _____

Part E

meat •

meet •

wood •

would •

• Did you _____ the train?

• Most people _____ like this show.

• something to eat

• something to build with

Part F

These words are in the puzzle.
Circle 7 or more of the words.

think   silk   park

judge   stop   grape

shop   cool   build

shore   leash   people

```
t  s  s  h  h  k
l  t  h  i  n  k
e  c  o  o  l  o
a  b  p  a  r  k
s  j  u  d  g  e
h  t  o  i  o  o
p  e  o  p  l  e
g  r  a  p  e  d
```

Lesson 12

Part A

1. _____   5. _____

2. _____   6. _____

3. _____   7. _____

4. _____   8. _____

Part B

1. _____   5. _____

2. _____   6. _____

3. _____   7. _____

4. _____   8. _____

Part C

1. _____

2. _____

3. _____

Part D

Draw a line from each word to its clue.

would •   • comes from cattle

meat •   • I'll _____ you at noon.

wood •   • We walked _____ the room.

meet •   • comes from trees

through •   • I _____ not say that.

Part E

Figure out each word and write it in the blank below.

thorau   ingldbui   chrea   ntoip

1. _____ 2. _____ 3. _____ 4. _____

Part F

Figure out the words in the second column and write them.
Then draw lines to the same words in the first column.

1. watched •   • __ __ __ g __

2. bridge •   • __ __ __ __ __ __

3. clock •   • __ __ __ __ __

4. listen •   • __ __ __ __ __ __

5. large •   • __ __ i __ __

Lesson 13

Part A

1. _____
2. _____
3. _____
4. _____
5. _____

6. _____
7. _____
8. _____
9. _____
10. _____

Part B

Graceful sailboats caught the rowboats.

_____

Part C

1. _____
2. _____
3. _____
4. _____

5. _____
6. _____
7. _____
8. _____

Part D

1. _ o _ _ _ _
2. _ _ _ t _ _
3. _ _ e _ _

4. _ _ _ _ t _
5. _ _ o u _ _ _

Part E

Draw a line from each word to its clue.

meat   •   • We aren't _____ yet.

through   •   • This house is made of _____.

meet   •   • How _____ you do this?

would   •   • The _____ is tough.

wood   •   • When did I _____ you?

Lesson 14

Part A

1. _____

2. _____

Part B

1. _____ 5. _____

2. _____ 6. _____

3. _____ 7. _____

4. _____ 8. _____

Part C

___ a c e ___ l ___ a i ___ o a ___ ___ a u g h ___

___ ___ ___ ___ o w ___ ___ ___ .

_____

Part D

1. _____ 4. _____

2. _____ 5. _____

3. _____ 6. _____

Part E

Draw a line from each word to its clue.

write   •   • We walked _____ the tunnel.

meat   •   • Can you _____ quickly?

wood   •   • That doll is made of _____.

through   •   • a type of food

Part F

Cross out the misspelled words in these sentences.
Then write the words correctly above the crossed-out words.

Eat your meet with your forck.

Peeple wached from the roof.

Lesson 15

Part A

1. _____

2. _____

Part B

1. _____   5. _____

2. _____   6. _____

3. _____   7. _____

4. _____   8. _____

Part C

__ __ a c __ __ __ __ __   __ a i __ __ __ a __ __   __ a u __ __ __

__ __ __   __ __ w __ __ __ __ __ .

_____

Part D

1. _____   5. _____

2. _____   6. _____

3. _____   7. _____

4. _____   8. _____

Part E

Figure out the words in the second column and write them.
Then draw lines to the same words in the first column.

1. charge   •   •   __ a __ __ __ __

2. fringe   •   •   __ h __ __ __ __

3. ridge   •   •   __ __ d __ __

4. change   •   •   __ __ i __ __ __

5. badge   •   •   __ __ __ n __

6. nudge   •   •   __ r __ __ __ __

Lesson 16

Part A

1. press
2. glass
3. boss
4. bliss
5. dress

6. class
7. mess
8. loss
9. hiss
10. fuss

Part B

1. _____

2. _____

Part C

1. _____
2. _____
3. _____
4. _____

5. _____
6. _____
7. _____
8. _____

Part D

_ _ _ c _ _ _ _ _   _ _ i _ _ _ _ _ _   _ _ u _ _ _

_ _ _   _ _ _ _ _ _ _ _ .

_____

Part E

These words are in the puzzle.
Circle 7 or more of the words.

brush	port	crash
press	happy	need
bound	wonder	spell
fill	mess	count

b b c b b m f
h p o r t e i
a r u u a s l
p e n s n s l
p s t h e d h
y s s p e l l
c w o n d e r

Lesson 17

Part A

How _____ you _____ this report?

Part B

glass	race
fuss	voice
press	fence
bliss	nice
boss	place
dress	choice

Part C

1. _____

2. _____

Part D

1. o _ _ _ _ _   4. _ u _ _ _ _ _ _

2. _ _ _ _ _ u _ _   5. _ _ _ _ e

3. _ _ _ _ i _ _ _   6. _ _ a _

Part E

Write each of these words in a box.

sell	brown	enough	huge	brush	choice	happy	join
fill	change	found	fence	crash	dress	race	think

Lesson 18

Part A

1. _____ ____

2. _____ ____

Part B

1. _____ 5. _____

2. _____ 6. _____

3. _____ 7. _____

4. _____ 8. _____

Part C

Eight children left school together.

_____

Part D

1. _ _ _ o _   4. _ _ _ i _ _

2. _ _ _ _ l _   5. _ _ _ _ _

3. _ _ _ p _   6. _ _ _ t _ _

Part E

Draw a line from each word to its clue.

through •   • I _____ like some sleep.

write •   • Let's _____ at the park.

would •   • They marched _____ town.

meet •   • We want _____ and potatoes.

their •   • They own _____ home.

meat •   • with a pencil

Lesson 19

Part A

1. _____   3. _____

2. _____   4. _____

Part B

1. _____

2. _____

Part C

1. _____   5. _____

2. _____   6. _____

3. _____   7. _____

4. _____   8. _____

Part D

E i _ _ _ _   _ _ i _ _ r e _   _ _ _ _ _   _ c h _ _ _ _

_ _ o _ e _ _ _ _ .

_____

Part E

rowboats	caught
friends	wonder
together	through
should	sailboats
building	people
bridge	voice
light	watched
tough	pledge
graceful	listen
thought	believe

Part F

Figure out the words in the second column and write them.
Then draw lines to the same words in the first column.

1. motor   •   • _ _ _ _ _ _ l _

2. should   •   • _ _ _ _ _ d

3. happy   •   • _ _ _ _ _ _ _

4. friend   •   • _ _ _ t _ _

5. grand   •   • _ _ _ _ t _ _

6. little   •   • _ _ _ _ _

Lesson 20

Part A

1. _____   4. _____

2. _____   5. _____

3. _____   6. _____

Part B

1. _____

2. _____

Part C

1. _____   5. _____

2. _____   6. _____

3. _____   7. _____

4. _____   8. _____

Part D

E _ _ _ _   _ _ i _ _ _ _ _   _ _ _ _   _ _ h _ _ _

_ _ _ e _ _ _ _.

_____

Part E

Cross out the misspelled words in these sentences.
Then write the words correctly above the crossed-out words.

I thought they wood lissen.

They love thair home.

Lesson 21

Part A

_____ _____ ____ _____

_____.

_____

Part B

1. ring	3. rent	5. water	7. fresh
2. wonder	4. act	6. pack	8. listen

Part C

1. _____ ring   5. _____ renting

2. _____ ringing   6. _____ react

3. _____ wondering   7. _____ watering

4. _____ wonder   8. _____ repacking

Part D

1. _____   3. _____

2. _____   4. _____

Part E

These words are in the puzzle.
Circle 7 or more of the words.

worth	count	shoot
ask	kept	write
wonder	stop	stone
shape	need	made

```
s c w r i t e
s w o n d e r
h s r u e s m
a s t o n e a
p s h o o t d
e v k e p t e
```

Lesson 22

Part A

1. _____

2. _____

Part B

1. rest	3. born	5. fresh	7. count	9. think
2. string	4. quiet	6. water	8. place	10. light

Part C

1. _____ resting   5. _____ quieting

2. _____ rest   6. _____ stringing

3. _____ string   7. _____ refreshing

4. _____ reborn   8. _____ watering

Part D

1. _____   3. _____

2. _____   4. _____

Part E

Draw a line from each word to its clue.

their	•	• When will you go _____?
right	•	• putting words on paper
through	•	• fuel for a fire
meet	•	• They found _____ money.
write	•	• a type of food
would	•	• not wrong
meat	•	• How _____ it feel to be a cat?
wood	•	• What time should we _____?

Lesson 23

Part A

1. fresh	4. wonder	7. lock	10. place
2. rest	5. ring	8. pack	11. press
3. rent	6. happy	9. build	12. spend

Part B

1. _____ refresh

2. _____ resting

3. _____ rest

4. _____ rent

5. _____ refreshing

6. _____ wondering

7. _____ ringing

8. _____ ring

Part C

1. _____

2. _____

3. _____

4. _____

5. _____

6. _____

7. _____

8. _____

Part D

1. _____

2. _____

3. _____

4. _____

Part E

1. _____ + _____ = building

2. _____ + _____ = replace

3. _____ + _____ = pressing

4. _____ + _____ + _____ = unpacking

5. _____ + _____ = spending

Part F

Cross out the misspelled words in these sentences.
Then write the words correctly above the crossed-out words.

Eite children left skool togather.

I beleve she is throogh.

Lesson 24

Part A

1. _____ fun

2. _____ unborn

3. _____ fresh

4. _____ refreshing

5. _____ unrefreshing

6. _____ unhappy

Part B

1. _____

2. _____

Part C

1. _____

2. _____

3. _____

4. _____

5. _____

6. _____

Part D

Fill in the blanks to show the morphographs in each word.

1. _____ + _____ = coldest

2. _____ + _____ = wondering

3. _____ + _____ + _____ = unfolding

4. _____ + _____ = listening

5. _____ + _____ = greenest

6. _____ + _____ + _____ = rebuilding

Part E

Figure out the words in the second column and write them.
Then draw lines to the same words in the first column.

1. glass •   • v_ _ _ _

2. voice •   • _ _ _ c _

3. change •   • _ _ _ _ _ _

4. bridge •   • _ _ _ _ e _

5. thick •   • _ u _ _

6. look •   • _ _ d _ _

7. large •   • _ _ _ s _

8. tough •   • _ _ _ _ _

Lesson 25

Part A

Draw a line from each morphograph to its meaning.

re •   • when you do something

ing •   • not

un •   • again

est •   • the most

Part B

1. _____
2. _____
3. _____
4. _____

5. _____
6. _____
7. _____
8. _____

Part C

-age   -ine   -oke

Part D

1. _____
2. _____

Part E

1. _____
2. _____
3. _____

4. _____
5. _____

Part F

Fill in the blanks to show the morphographs in each word.

1. _____ + _____ = refine
2. _____ + _____ = unsound
3. _____ + _____ = brownest
4. _____ + _____ = dressing
5. _____ + _____ + _____ = unkindest
6. _____ + _____ + _____ = unthinking

Lesson 26

Part A

-ake   -ide   -obe

Part B

Draw a line from each morphograph to its meaning.

re   •   • when you do something

ing   •   • without

un   •   • again

est   •   • the most

less •   • not

Part C

1. __ a ____

2. _____ i ___

3. __ o r ___

4. _____

5. _____ e __

6. ___ u ___

Part D

1. _____   4. _____

2. _____   5. _____

3. _____   6. _____

Part E

Fill in the blanks to show the morphographs in each word.

1. _____ + _____ = friendless

2. _____ + _____ + _____ = unthinking

3. _____ + _____ + _____ = unkindest

4. _____ + _____ = worthless

5. _____ + _____ = rewrite

6. _____ + _____ = lightest

Lesson 27

Part A

1. _____   5. _____

2. _____   6. _____

3. _____   7. _____

4. _____   8. _____

Part B

1. _____

2. _____

Part C

1. _____   4. _____

2. _____   5. _____

3. _____   6. _____

Part D

could	luck	real	book	want
reach	room	skill	listen	fight
these	those	spend	above	which
graceful	try	need	trick	trust
pledge	count	sold	change	tough

Part E

Draw a line from each morphograph to its meaning.

mis •   • not

less •   • again

est •   • wrong

un •   • when you do something

re •   • the most

ing •   • without

Lesson 28

Part A

       equal   serve   human   great

Part B

The author wrote several different stories.

_____

Part C

Fill in the blanks to show the morphographs in each word.

1. _____ + _____ + _____ = misspelling

2. _____ + _____ = unhappy

3. _____ + _____ + _____ = repacking

4. _____ + _____ = unclear

5. _____ + _____ = quietest

6. _____ + _____ = mistake

Part D

Draw a line from each word to its clue.

there •   • I would like to _____ a story.

right •   • They love _____ children.

meat •   • I _____ not touch that.

would •   • get together

through •   • We found them over _____.

their •   • This is not wrong. It's _____.

write •   • The ball went _____ the window.

meet •   • The _____ is tough.

Lesson 29

Part A

1. _____   5. _____

2. _____   6. _____

3. _____   7. _____

4. _____   8. _____

Part B

_____ __u___o__ w_____ _____e__a__

_____e_r_e__ _____i_e__.

_____

Part C

motor	friend	since	boss	could
human	happy	gold	great	equal
real	tough	believe	need	replace
want	these	city	bridge	people

Part D

Draw a line from each morphograph to its meaning.

un   •   • the most

mis   •   • again

re   •   • without

ing   •   • not

est   •   • when you do something

less   •   • wrong

Part E

These words are in the puzzle
Circle 7 or more of the words.

human	city	most
rest	made	author
done	above	serve
cube	great	ends

```
s e r v e h
h a r r n u
c u b e d m
i t m o s t
t h a a v t
y o d o n e
g r e a t t
```

Lesson 30

Part A

1. _____   4. _____
2. _____   5. _____
3. _____   6. _____

Part B

___ ___ ___ ___ u ___ o w ___ ___ ___ ___ ___ ___ ___ a ___

___ ___ ___ e ___ e ___ ___ ___ ___ ___ ___ i ___.

_____

Part C

1. _____ 11. _____ 21. _____
2. _____ 12. _____ 22. _____
3. _____ 13. _____ 23. _____
4. _____ 14. _____ 24. _____
5. _____ 15. _____ 25. _____
6. _____ 16. _____ 26. _____
7. _____ 17. _____ 27. _____
8. _____ 18. _____ 28. _____
9. _____ 19. _____ 29. _____
10. _____ 20. _____ 30. _____

Part D

Figure out the words in the second column and write them.
Then draw lines to the same words in the first column.

1. here •   • __ __ o __ __

2. there •   • __ __ __ __ __

3. where •   • __ __ __ s __

4. these •   • __ l __ __ __

5. those •   • __ __ __ __ __

6. close •   • w __ __ __ __

Lesson 31

Part A

charm   cheap   child   choke   chalk   chill

Part B

1. _____   5. _____

2. _____   6. _____

3. _____   7. _____

4. _____   8. _____

Part C

__ __ __   __ u __ __ __   w __ __ __ __   __ __ __ __ __ a __

__ __ __ __ __ __ e __ __   __ __ __ __ i __ __.

_____

Part D

value   break   length   strength

Part E

Draw a line from each morphograph to its meaning.

un •   • wrong

less •   • not

re •   • when you do something

est •   • again

ing •   • without

mis •   • the most

Part F

Fill in the blanks to show the morphographs in each word.

1. _____ + _____ + _____ = misspelling

2. _____ + _____ = unequal

3. _____ + _____ = greatest

4. _____ + _____ = pointless

5. _____ + _____ = rewrite

6. _____ + _____ = charming

Lesson 32

Part A

b u h o t e i n c

a f r u s g i m o

Part B

1. _____   5. _____

2. _____   6. _____

3. _____   7. _____

4. _____   8. _____

Part C

1. _____

2. _____

Part D

1. _____   4. _____

2. _____   5. _____

3. _____   6. _____

Part E

Cross out the misspelled words in these sentences.
Then write the words correctly above the crossed-out words.

The freinds did not have equil strength.

My dog acts like a humen.

I thowght that I wanted to werk hard.

Lesson 33

Part A

Make a small **v** above every vowel letter.
Make a small **c** above every consonant letter.

n e c j k o v d l

p a r f u e i o t

Part B

1. _____   5. _____

2. _____   6. _____

3. _____   7. _____

4. _____   8. _____

Part C

1. _____

2. _____

Part D

1. _____   4. _____

2. _____   5. _____

3. _____   6. _____

Part E

Draw a line from each word to its clue.

feat •   • they own it

there •   • Why did you _____ that note?

write •   • great skill

meat •   • We put the thread _____ the needle.

their •   • Where _____ they put this?

right •   • We found the toys over _____.

would •   • correct

through •   • I like cold _____ and gravy.

Lesson 34

Part A

-atch   -etch   -itch   -otch

Part B

1. _____

2. _____

Part C

1. _____
2. _____
3. _____
4. _____
5. _____
6. _____

Part D

Write each of these words in a box.

size	wrote	repay	cure
helpless	fire	there	large
want	strength	charming	eight
workable	judge	school	these

Part E

Make a small **v** above every vowel letter.
Make a small **c** above every consonant letter.

a   c   i   m   s   u   d   o   p

v   e   o   u   n   t   z   r   k

Lesson 35

Part A

      -atch   -etch   -itch   -otch

Part B

1. _____   4. _____

2. _____   5. _____

3. _____   6. _____

Part C

1. _____

2. _____

Part D

Fill in the blanks to show the morphographs in each word.

1. _____ + _____ = report

2. _____ + _____ = portable

3. _____ + _____ + _____ = unworkable

4. _____ + _____ = roughness

5. _____ + _____ + _____ = thoughtlessness

6. _____ + _____ + _____ = misspelling

7. _____ + _____ + _____ = unbreakable

Part E

Make a small **v** above every vowel letter.
Make a small **c** above every consonant letter.

     u   b   n   i   o   k   l

     a   e   g   t   i   h   a

Lesson 36

Part A

1. <u>c</u>at<u>ch</u>

2. <u>d</u>it<u>ch</u>

3. <u>n</u>ot<u>ch</u>

4. <u>m</u>at<u>ch</u>

5. stretch

6. st<u>itch</u>

Part B

Write the word for each meaning.

word

1. _____
2. _____
3. _____
4. _____
5. _____
6. _____

meaning

not sure

without need

build again

that which is quiet

judge wrong

able to be washed

Part C

1. _____
2. _____
3. _____

4. _____
5. _____
6. _____

Part D

Make a small **v** above every vowel letter.
Make a small **c** above every consonant letter.

b   r   e   n   o   p   z

i   a   j   u   k   i   e

Part E

Draw a line from each morphograph
to its meaning.

able   •   •   in the past

mis   •   •   able to be

ed   •   •   without

re   •   •   that which is

less   •   •   not

ing   •   •   wrong

ness   •   •   when you do
                                something

un   •   •   again

Lesson 37

Part A

civil   search   touch   view

Part B

1. _____   4. _____

2. _____   5. _____

3. _____   6. _____

Part C

1. _____   4. _____

2. _____   5. _____

3. _____   6. _____

Part D

Write the word for each meaning.

word	meaning
1. _____	help in the past
2. _____	that which is dark
3. _____	able to work
4. _____	not happy
5. _____	spell wrong
6. _____	without rest

Part E

Fill in the blanks to show the morphographs in each word.

1. _____ + _____ + _____ = unkindest

2. _____ + _____ + _____ = repacked

3. _____ + _____ + _____ = pointlessness

4. _____ + _____ = remark

5. _____ + _____ = roughness

6. _____ + _____ + _____ = mismatched

7. _____ + _____ = brushing

8. _____ + _____ + _____ = unsoundness

Lesson 38

Part A

1. _____

2. _____

3. _____

4. _____

5. _____

6. _____

Part B

1. _____

2. _____

Part C

1. _____ n _____

2. _ i e _

3. _____ i _

4. _ o u c _

5. _ e a _

6. _ e _ _

Part D

1. like + able = _____

2. write + ing = _____

3. smoke + ing = _____

4. green + est = _____

5. pure + est = _____

6. use + able = _____

7. shine + ing = _____

8. dark + ness = _____

Part E

Draw a line from each word to its clue.

feet •   • Put your things over _____.

witch •   • not left

there •   • Let's _____ before school.

feat •   • The fire jumper landed on her _____.

right •   • This _____ is very hard.

their •   • doing something great

wood •   • someone with magical powers

meet •   • They like _____ new game.

Lesson 39

Part A

1. _____   4. _____

2. _____   5. _____

3. _____   6. _____

Part B

1. _____

2. _____

Part C

1. fine + est   = _____

2. cure + able = _____

3. ripe + ness = _____

4. worth + less = _____

5. hope + less = _____

6. stage + ing = _____

7. judge + ed   = _____

8. shame + less = _____

Part D

Write each of these words in a box.

through	value	touch	sack
grounded	replace	search	view
change	mistake	large	since
break	bridge	length	worth

Part E

Write the word for each meaning.

word	**meaning**
1. _____	start in the past
2. _____	without worth
3. _____	the most fresh
4. _____	shrunk before
5. _____	without speech
6. _____	that which is cold

Lesson 40

Part A

1. _____   4. _____

2. _____   5. _____

3. _____   6. _____

Part B

1. _____

2. _____

Part C

1. _____   5. _____

2. _____   6. _____

3. _____   7. _____

4. _____   8. _____

Part D

Add these morphographs together.
Some of the words follow the rule about dropping an **e**.

1. large + est   = _____

2. change + less = _____

3. race + ing   = _____

4. fine + ness   = _____

5. work + able   = _____

6. hire + ed   = _____

7. wide + est   = _____

8. shape + ing   = _____

Part E

1. _____

2. _____

3. _____

4. _____

5. _____

6. _____

Part F

Draw a line from each morphograph to its meaning.

ed   •   • before

able •   • in the past

ness •   • wrong

pre   •   • that which is

re   •   • again

mis   •   • able to be

Lesson 41

Part A

1. There is a <u>larje</u> house over there. Ⓡ Ⓦ
2. Don't walk over that <u>brige</u>. Ⓡ Ⓦ
3. I found a <u>worthless</u> coin. Ⓡ Ⓦ
4. Were you <u>lissening</u> to me? Ⓡ Ⓦ
5. We <u>should</u> know that answer. Ⓡ Ⓦ
6. Those people like <u>there</u> home. Ⓡ Ⓦ

Part B

1. k __ __ w
2. __ __ __ g h __
3. __ __ u __ __ __
4. __ __ r __ __ __
5. __ __ __ e __
6. __ __ __ s __ __ __ __

Part C

1. _____ + _____ = _____
2. _____ + _____ = _____
3. _____ + _____ = _____
4. _____ + _____ = _____
5. _____ + _____ = _____
6. _____ + _____ = _____

Part D

Wash the clothes with the new soap.

_____

Part E

Fill in the blanks to show the morphographs in each word.

1. _____ + _____ = boundless
2. _____ + _____ + _____ = unbreakable
3. _____ + _____ + _____ = helplessness
4. _____ + _____ + _____ = misspelling
5. _____ + _____ + _____ = refillable
6. _____ + _____ = building
7. _____ + _____ = colder
8. _____ + _____ + _____ + _____ = unrefreshing

Lesson 42

Part A

Fill in the circle marked **R** if the underlined word is spelled right.
Fill in the circle marked **W** if the underlined word is spelled wrong.

1. They found the boys <u>togather</u>. Ⓡ Ⓦ

2. Can you <u>teach</u> me that trick? Ⓡ Ⓦ

3. I will see you after <u>skool</u>. Ⓡ Ⓦ

4. We have <u>sevral</u> different coins. Ⓡ Ⓦ

5. That answer isn't <u>write</u>. Ⓡ Ⓦ

6. Did you <u>misspell</u> that word? Ⓡ Ⓦ

Part B

1. _____ + _____ = _____

2. _____ + _____ = _____

3. _____ + _____ = _____

4. _____ + _____ = _____

5. _____ + _____ = _____

6. _____ + _____ = _____

Part C

_ a _ _   _ _ _   _ _ _ _ _ e s   _ _ _ _ _

_ _ _   _ e w   _ o a _ .

Part D

1. _____

2. _____

3. _____

4. _____

5. _____

6. _____

7. _____

8. _____

Part E

Draw a line from each morphograph to its meaning.

ly •   • in the past

ness •   • not

mis •   • that which is

un •   • how something is

pre •   • more, one who

er •   • without

less •   • wrong

ed •   • before

Lesson 43

Part A

1. _____ + _____ = _____
2. _____ + _____ = _____
3. _____ + _____ = _____
4. _____ + _____ = _____
5. _____ + _____ = _____
6. _____ + _____ = _____

Part B

__ a __ __   __ __ __ __   __ __ __ __ __ e __   __ __ __ __ __

__ __ __   __ __ w __   __ __ a __ __ .

_____

Part C

1. _____   4. _____
2. _____   5. _____
3. _____   6. _____

Part D

review	serve	witch	ridge	value	right	trick	choice
touch	human	worthless	listening	break	meat	think	cure
search	great	were	hold	length	would	stop	believe
civil	feat	unhappy	fence	equal	their	spelling	building

Part E

Fill in the circle marked **R** is the underlined word is spelled right.
Fill in the circle marked **W** if the underlined word is spelled wrong.

1. Those peeple are very nice.   (R)   (W)
2. How many children are here?   (R)   (W)
3. They can't find there sister.   (R)   (W)
4. This balloon won't strech any further.   (R)   (W)
5. Who is the auther of this story?   (R)   (W)
6. I would like to look for gold.   (R)   (W)

Lesson 44

Part A

1. _____ + _____ = tracing
2. _____ + _____ = careless
3. _____ + _____ = faced
4. _____ + _____ = usable
5. _____ + _____ = likely
6. _____ + _____ = sizable

Part B

———— ——— —————— ————
——— ——— ————.

_____

Part C

1. _____   5. _____
2. _____   6. _____
3. _____   7. _____
4. _____   8. _____

Part D

Add these morphographs together.
Some of the words follow the rule about dropping an **e**.

1. re + place + ed = _____

2. hope + less + ly = _____

3. re + serve + ed = _____

4. pre + view + ed = _____

5. un + use + able = _____

6. un + equal + ly = _____

Part E

above	speech
blue	shortest
should	restless
quietly	useless
locker	switch
class	pure

Part F

These words are in the puzzle.
Circle 7 or more of the words.

counting	point	joined
jet	smart	found
sprint	neat	lost
sigh	bring	new

```
p  j  f  l  c  s  m
s  o  e  o  o  l  t
m  i  i  t  u  s  t
a  n  g  n  n  n  t
r  e  e  h  t  e  d
t  d  s  w  i  a  d
s  p  r  i  n  t  g
b  r  i  n  g  g  d
```

Lesson 45

Part A

1. _____

2. _____

Part B

1. _____
2. _____
3. _____
4. _____
5. _____
6. _____
7. _____
8. _____
9. _____
10. _____
11. _____
12. _____
13. _____
14. _____
15. _____

16. _____
17. _____
18. _____
19. _____
20. _____
21. _____
22. _____
23. _____
24. _____
25. _____
26. _____
27. _____
28. _____
29. _____
30. _____

31. _____
32. _____
33. _____
34. _____
35. _____
36. _____
37. _____
38. _____
39. _____
40. _____
41. _____
42. _____
43. _____
44. _____
45. _____

Part C

Add these morphographs together.
Some of the words follow the rule about dropping an **e.**

1. time + less   = _____

2. serve + ing   = _____

3. cure + able   = _____

4. mis + place + ed = _____

5. smile + ing   = _____

6. bright + est   = _____

7. wide + ly   = _____

8. chime + ing   = _____

Lesson 46

Part A

1. _____

2. _____

Part B

1. _____

2. _____

3. _____

4. _____

5. _____

6. _____

52

Part C

Write each word in a box.

harmlessly valuable   fright   brightness
unreachable sketching every   slightest
preserve   stretcher civil   nightly
fighter   preshrunk catcher   length

Part D

Fill in the blanks to show the morphographs in each word.

1. _____ + _____ + _____ = preserving

2. _____ + _____ + _____ = rehiring

3. _____ + _____ = blameless

4. _____ + _____ + _____ = uselessness

5. _____ + _____ + _____ = unlikely

6. _____ + _____ = listening

7. _____ + _____ + _____ = resorted

8. _____ + _____ = bluest

Part E

Draw a line from each word to its clue.

witch •   • I don't know _____ I like better.

feat •   • Put these things _____, please.

which •   • get together

wood •   • The _____ is dressed in black.

meet •   • Will you _____ me a letter?

write •   • not wrong

there •   • something great

right •   • We burn _____ in our stove.

Lesson 47

Part A

     bite   kite   quite   white   spite

Part B

1. _____

2. _____

Part C

1. _____

2. _____

3. _____

4. _____

5. _____

6. _____

Part D

Fill in the blanks to show the morphographs in each word.

1. _____ + _____ = fineness

2. _____ + _____ = sizable

3. _____ + _____ = biting

4. _____ + _____ + _____ = replaced

5. _____ + _____ + _____ = misjudged

6. _____ + _____ = namely

7. _____ + _____ = shameless

8. _____ + _____ = fired

Part E

ly	•	• not
er	•	• in the past
pre	•	• when you do something
ed	•	• more, one who
able	•	• able to be
ness	•	• wrong
mis	•	• how something is
less	•	• the most
est	•	• again
un	•	• before
ing	•	• that which is
re	•	• without

Lesson 48

Part A

1. _____
2. _____
3. _____
4. _____
5. _____

6. _____
7. _____
8. _____
9. _____
10. _____

Part B

1. C _ _ _ _
2. _ _ _ _ _
3. _ _ W _
4. _ _ i _ _
5. _ _ l _
6. _ _ _ s _

Part C

Add these morphographs together.
Some of the words follow the rule about dropping an **e**.

1. race + ing = _____
2. re + name + ing = _____
3. white + est = _____
4. probe + ing = _____
5. pure + ness = _____
6. wide + ly = _____
7. bake + er = _____
8. life + less = _____

Part D

Write the word for each meaning.

word	meaning
1. _____	build again
2. _____	judge wrong
3. _____	able to work
4. _____	the most kind
5. _____	that which is good
6. _____	without a home
7. _____	one who teaches
8. _____	not sold

Lesson 49

Part A

1. pack	3. big	5. plan	7. stop	9. clap
2. flat	4. wonder	6. charm	8. civil	10. fit

Part B

1. _____

2. _____

Part C

able	cure	work	ing	un	like

1. _____   5. _____

2. _____   6. _____

3. _____   7. _____

4. _____   8. _____

Part D

Fill in the blanks to show the morphographs in each word.

1. _____ + _____ + _____ = previewed

2. _____ + _____ + _____ = unequally

3. _____ + _____ = whitest

4. _____ + _____ + _____ = unusable

5. _____ + _____ + _____ = researching

6. _____ + _____ + _____ = thoughtlessly

7. _____ + _____ = valuable

8. _____ + _____ = civilly

Part E

Cross out the misspelled words in these sentences.
Then write the words correctly above the crossed-out words.

My friend rote a towching story.

That illness is not cureable.

Lesson 50

Part A

1. _ _ _ _ e _ _

2. _ _ _ _ _ _ _

3. _ _ _ _ _ n g _ _

4. _ _ _ _ _ _ _ _

5. _ _ _ u _ _ _ _

6. _ _ _ _ _ _ _

Part B

1. flop

2. human

3. star

4. kite

5. drag

6. list

7. run

8. snap

9. plan

10. water

Part C

like	able	ing	stretch	note	ed	use

1. _____

2. _____

3. _____

4. _____

5. _____

6. _____

7. _____

8. _____

9. _____

10. _____

11. _____

Part D

Draw a line from each morphograph to its meaning.

mis •   • in the past

ness •   • not

less •   • that which is

able •   • one who, more

ed •   • wrong

est •   • before

pre •   • without

un •   • how something is

re •   • when you do something

er •   • able to be

ing •   • the most

ly •   • again

Lesson 51

Part A

That person often paints pictures.

_____

Part B

1. _____   4. _____

2. _____   5. _____

3. _____   6. _____

Part C

Circle each short word that ends **cvc**.
Remember, short words have four letters or less.

1. plan   3. arm   5. step   7. trip

2. rest   4. big   6. brother   8. drop

Part D

1. _____

2. _____

Part E

Add these morphographs together.
Some of the words follow the rule about dropping an **e**.

1. value + able = _____

2. like + ing   = _____

3. fine + er   = _____

4. fine + ness = _____

5. fine + ly   = _____

6. time + less = _____

7. use + less   = _____

8. use + ing   = _____

9. trace + ing = _____

10. safe + ly   = _____

11. wide + ness = _____

12. wide + ly   = _____

13. wide + est   = _____

14. serve + ing = _____

15. love + able = _____

Lesson 52

Part A

1. _____   5. _____

2. _____   6. _____

3. _____   7. _____

4. _____   8. _____

Part B

____ ____o__ __te_ _ai___

__ctue__.

_____

Part C

1. _i____   3. ____l__   5. _____

2. ___a__   4. _____

Part D

1. _____ + _____ = _____

2. _____ + _____ = _____

3. _____ + _____ = _____

4. _____ + _____ = _____

5. _____ + _____ = _____

6. _____ + _____ = _____

Part E

Circle each short word that ends **cvc**.
Remember, short words have four letters or less.

1. motor   3. time   5. spot   7. fill

2. mad   4. smell   6. run   8. drop

Part F

Fill in the blanks to show the morphographs in each word.

1. _____ + _____ + _____ = helplessness

2. _____ + _____ = quietly

3. _____ + _____ = formless

4. _____ + _____ = friendly

5. _____ + _____ = stretcher

6. _____ + _____ + _____ = unpacked

7. _____ + _____ = timely

8. _____ + _____ = serving

9. _____ + _____ = staging

10. _____ + _____ = ripeness

Lesson 53

Part A

_____ _____o_ __t__ _a_____

_____t u_____.

Part B

Add these morphographs together.
Some of the words follow the rule about dropping an **e**.

1. slight + est = _____

2. nice + est = _____

3. care + ing = _____

4. un + work + able = _____

5. pre + serve + ing = _____

6. de + serve + ed = _____

Part C

Draw a line from each morphograph to its meaning.

de •   • how something is

ly •   • that which is

ness •   • in the past

pre •   • more, one who

re •   • down, away from

er •   • again

less •   • without

ed •   • before

Part D

These words are in the puzzle.
Circle 7 or more of the words.

speller	deal	city
hear	spend	rake
serve	care	press
grade	have	part

```
s s s d p s g
s p p e a h r
p h e a r a a
c c n l t v d
i a d l l e e
t r r a k e e
y p r e s s r
```

Lesson 54

Part A

Double when cvc + v

1. run + er   = _____

2. water + ed = _____

3. sad + ness = _____

4. help + ful = _____

5. swim + ing = _____

6. mad + ly   = _____

7. form + less = _____

8. sad + er   = _____

Part B

____ _____ ____ _____

_____.

Part C

1. _____ 5. _____

2. _____ 6. _____

3. _____ 7. _____

4. _____ 8. _____

Part D

Fill in the blanks to show the morphographs in each word.

1. _____ + _____ + _____ = redefine

2. _____ + _____ + _____ = unequally

3. _____ + _____ = forceful

4. _____ + _____ + _____ = reserved

5. _____ + _____ = choicest

6. _____ + _____ + _____ + _____ = unrefined

7. _____ + _____ + _____ = misused

8. _____ + _____ = devalue

Part E

Write the word for each meaning.

	word	meaning
1.	_____	that which is thick
2.	_____	stretch in the past
3.	_____	the most fresh
4.	_____	full of help
5.	_____	shrunk before
6.	_____	the most grand
7.	_____	one who fights
8.	_____	more white

Lesson 55

Part A

sign   fault   care   bare   carry

Part B

hope   slope   rope   scope   cope

Part C

1. _____

2. _____

Part D

Double when cvc + v

1. bar + ed   = _____

2. snap + ing   = _____

3. mad + ness = _____

4. plan + ed   = _____

5. water + ed = _____

6. wash + able = _____

7. shop + ing = _____

8. run + er   = _____

Part E

less	care	rest	ed	ful	ing	hope

1. _____   7. _____

2. _____   8. _____

3. _____   9. _____

4. _____   10. _____

5. _____   11. _____

6. _____

Part F

Draw a line from each morphograph to its meaning.

ful •　　　• before

de •　　　• more, one who

ly •　　　• down, away from

er •　　　• in the past

pre •　　　• that which is

ness •　　　• without

less •　　　• full of

ed •　　　• how something is

Lesson 56

Part A

1. _ _ _ _ _

2. _ _ g _ _

3. _ _ _ _ _

4. _ _ u _ _

5. _ _ _ r _

6. _ _ _ _ e

Part B

Double when cvc + v

1. stop + ing = _____

2. fit + ness = _____

3. farm + er = _____

4. sad + ness = _____

5. plan + ed = _____

6. bliss + ful = _____

7. human + ness = _____

8. sad + en = _____

Part C

Fill in the circle marked **R** if the underlined word is spelled right.
Fill in the circle marked **W** if the underlined word is spelled wrong.

1. Is that a <u>which</u> on that broom?   Ⓡ   Ⓦ

2. We like that <u>persen</u> very much.   Ⓡ   Ⓦ

3. They shared the money <u>equally</u>.   Ⓡ   Ⓦ

4. I was <u>hopeing</u> you would be there.   Ⓡ   Ⓦ

5. Is that ball made from <u>would</u> or rubber?   Ⓡ   Ⓦ

6. He <u>misjuged</u> her strength.   Ⓡ   Ⓦ

Part D

Draw a line from each word to its clue.

tail •   • My _____ are too big for these shoes.

feat •   • I don't know _____ puppy to pick.

feet •   • correct

tale •   • That monkey has a long _____.

write •   • Those people lost _____ way.

which •   • How quickly can you _____?

their •   • something great

right •   • a story

Lesson 57

Part A

1. _____

2. _____

Part B

1. _____   5. _____

2. _____   6. _____

3. _____   7. _____

4. _____

Part C

1. stop + ing   = _____
2. fit + ness   = _____
3. shop + ed   = _____
4. farm + er   = _____

5. swim + er   = _____
6. mad + ness = _____
7. sad + ly   = _____
8. trip + ed   = _____

Part D

1. face
   unnamed
   trase
   friendly

   _____

2. awthor
   freshness
   equal
   motor

   _____

3. spelling
   stretch
   author
   happey

   _____

4. change
   sirve
   trace
   reserve

   _____

5. blissful
   force
   preserve
   moter

   _____

6. page
   chandge
   stretcher
   match

   _____

Part E

Add these morphographs together.
Some of the words follow the rule about dropping an **e.**

1. civil + ly   = _____
2. un + change + ing   = _____
3. gold + en   = _____
4. de + fine + ed   = _____
5. pack + age + ing   = _____
6. de + code + ing   = _____
7. un + ripe + en +ed   = _____
8. hope + ful + ly   = _____
9. de + light + ed   = _____
10. value + able   = _____

Lesson 58

Part A

world   wander   nerve   verb   herb

Part B

Circle the misspelled word in each group.
Then write it correctly on the line.

1. strength
   friendly
   pichure
   equally

   _____

2. juge
   preview
   listen
   nicely

   _____

3. nightly
   thaught
   touch
   spelling

   _____

4. mispell
   carry
   widely
   unpacked

   _____

5. stretch
   watch
   reatch
   switch

   _____

6. motor
   lightest
   preserve
   helplesness

   _____

Part C

1. star + ing   = _____
2. talk + ed   = _____
3. hot + ly   = _____
4. plan + er   = _____
5. big + est   = _____
6. grand + ly   = _____
7. sad + ness   = _____
8. mad + ness   = _____
9. step + ing   = _____
10. win + er   = _____

Part D

Part E

en • • more, one who

ful • • down, away from

de • • that which is

ly • • without

pre • • make

ness • • again

er • • full of

re • • when you do something

less • • how something is

ing • • before

Lesson 59

Part A

time	er	help	smoke	less	ed	use

1. _____
2. _____
3. _____
4. _____
5. _____
6. _____

7. _____
8. _____
9. _____
10. _____
11. _____

Part B

1. _____
2. _____
3. _____
4. _____

5. _____
6. _____
7. _____
8. _____

Part C

1. _____ + _____ = _____
2. _____ + _____ = _____
3. _____ + _____ = _____
4. _____ + _____ = _____
5. _____ + _____ = _____
6. _____ + _____ = _____

Part D

quietest	likely	design	brightest
paints	rope	searched	cheapest
patch	sailboat	jointly	motor
noise	writing	grandest	pictures
nerve	unreachable	faced	restlessness
mistaken	touched	breakable	scratched

Part E

Add these morphographs together.
Remember to use your spelling rules.

1. sign + al   = _____

2. fault + less   = _____

3. person + able   = _____

4. globe + al   = _____

5. use + age   = _____

6. weak + en   = _____

7. de + sign   = _____

8. re + coil + ed   = _____

9. de + serve + ing   = _____

10. un + equal + ly   = _____

Lesson 60

Part A

1. _____   5. _____

2. _____   6. _____

3. _____   7. _____

4. _____   8. _____

Part B

1. _____

2. _____

Part C

1. _____ + _____ = _____
2. _____ + _____ = _____
3. _____ + _____ = _____
4. _____ + _____ = _____
5. _____ + _____ = _____
6. _____ + _____ = _____

Part D

previewed	judging	city	restlessness
pictures	bare	shining	replaced
packages	hopeful	talker	mistaken
nicely	firing	tracing	breakable
motor	believable	useless	cheapest
lovable	catcher	scratched	unreachable

Part E

Circle the misspelled word in each group.
Then write it correctly in the blank.

1. cownt	2. touching	3. helpful
hoping	widest	search
people	carrey	greatest
shine	beetle	misplase
_____	_____	_____
4. patch	5. winner	6. strenght
older	watering	stretcher
holdding	valueing	toughness
cheaper	unkindness	together
_____	_____	_____

Lesson 61

Part A

1. happy
2. boy
3. you
4. yellow

5. berry
6. sturdy
7. play

Part B

1. _____ + _____ = _____
2. _____ + _____ = _____
3. _____ + _____ = _____
4. _____ + _____ = _____
5. _____ + _____ = _____
6. _____ + _____ = _____

Part C

1. _____
2. _____
3. _____
4. _____
5. _____
6. _____
7. _____
8. _____
9. _____
10. _____
11. _____
12. _____
13. _____
14. _____

15. _____
16. _____
17. _____
18. _____
19. _____
20. _____
21. _____
22. _____
23. _____
24. _____
25. _____
26. _____
27. _____

28. _____
29. _____
30. _____
31. _____
32. _____
33. _____
34. _____
35. _____
36. _____
37. _____
38. _____
39. _____
40. _____

74

Part D

1. _____ + _____ = swimmer
2. _____ + _____ = running
3. _____ + _____ = barely
4. _____ + _____ = driving
5. _____ + _____ = equally
6. _____ + _____ = maddest

Part E

Add these morphographs together.

1. large + ly   = _____
2. take + en   = _____
3. dose + age = _____
4. globe + al = _____
5. change + ing = _____
6. pack + age + ing = _____

Lesson 62

Part A

1. _____ + _____ = _____
2. _____ + _____ = _____
3. _____ + _____ = _____
4. _____ + _____ = _____
5. _____ + _____ = _____
6. _____ + _____ = _____

Part B

1. _____
2. _____

Part C

Fill in the blanks to show the morphographs in each word.

1. _____ + _____ = trapped
2. _____ + _____ = brownish
3. _____ + _____ = yardage
4. _____ + _____ = dripping
5. _____ + _____ = slipped
6. _____ + _____ = rental
7. _____ + _____ + _____ = delightful
8. _____ + _____ = design
9. _____ + _____ = signal
10. _____ + _____ + _____ = unsnapped

Part D

Make 10 real words from the morphographs in the box.

like	wide	en	ing	ness	length	take	ly

1. _____
2. _____
3. _____
4. _____
5. _____

6. _____
7. _____
8. _____
9. _____
10. _____

Lesson 63

Part A

1. _____
2. _____
3. _____

4. _____
5. _____
6. _____

Part B

1. _____ + _____ = _____
2. _____ + _____ = _____
3. _____ + _____ = _____
4. _____ + _____ = _____
5. _____ + _____ = _____
6. _____ + _____ = _____

Part C

Add these morphographs together.
Some of the words follow the rule about dropping an **e**.

1. give + en = _____
2. fool + ish + ly = _____
3. fine + al + ly = _____
4. store + age = _____
5. un + shake + en = _____
6. thought + ful + ly = _____
7. un + de + feat + ed = _____
8. pre + date + ed = _____
9. mis + shape + ed = _____
10. un + drink + able = _____
11. strength + en + ed = _____
12. wander + ing = _____

Part D

Cross out the misspelled words in these sentences.
Then write the words correctly above the crossed-out words.

Have you replased that worthless moter?

Witch small town is the nicest?

Lesson 64

7

Part A

note   vote   quote

Part B

We heard them try to deny the facts.

_____

Part C

1. _____ + _____ = _____
2. _____ + _____ = _____
3. _____ + _____ = _____
4. _____ + _____ = _____
5. _____ + _____ = _____
6. _____ + _____ = _____

Part D

Circle each short word that ends **cvc**.
Remember: short words have four letters or less
        y is a vowel letter at the end of a morphograph.

1. skin   3. spin   5. play   7. grab   9. stay   11. slam

2. tray   4. wander   6. person   8. ship   10. fit   12. bar

Part E

Add these morphographs together.
Some of the words follow the rule about dropping an **e**.

1. quote + able   = _____
2. re + fuse + al   = _____
3. child + ish + ly = _____
4. store + age   = _____
5. sign + al   = _____
6. de + sign + er = _____
7. person + able   = _____
8. use + ful + ly   = _____
9. rise + en   = _____
10. un + nerve + ed = _____

Lesson 65

Part A

wreck   wrote   write   wrong   wrap

Part B

__ __   _e a__   ____   __y   __   _e__y

___   _____.

_____

Part C

1. _____   5. _____

2. _____   6. _____

3. _____   7. _____

4. _____   8. _____

Part D

Add these morphographs together.
Some of the words follow the rule about doubling the final **c** in short words.

1. leak + age   = _____

2. slip + ed   = _____

3. star + less = _____

4. win + ing   = _____

5. norm + al   = _____

6. flat + en   = _____

7. drip + ed   = _____

8. snug + ly   = _____

Part E

Draw a line from each word to its clue.

whole •   • Have you heard that _____ before?

hear •   • _____ vegetable do you like the most?

here •   • Can you eat a _____ watermelon?

tale •   • correct

tail •   • putting words on paper

which •   • I can _____ you quite well.

write •   • Those things belong _____ .

right •   • they own it

their •   • part of an animal

Lesson 66

Part A

source   style   straight   prove

Part B

1. _____

2. _____

Part C

1. W _ _ _ _ _

2. W _ _ _ _

3. W _ _ _ _ _

4. W _ _ _ _ _

5. W _ _ _ _ _

Part D

___ __e a _____ ____ __ ____y

____ _____.

_____

Part E

mistaken	pointless	unquotable
previewed	people	stretching
lengthening	equal	golden
valuable	formal	harmlessly
person	resign	faultless
swimmer	lighten	largely

Part F

Fill in the blanks to show the morphographs in each word.

1. _____ + _____ + _____ = boyishness

2. _____ + _____ + _____ = departed

3. _____ + _____ + _____ = mistaken

4. _____ + _____ + _____ = resigned

5. _____ + _____ + _____ + _____ = unreserved

6. _____ + _____ + _____ = rightfully

7. _____ + _____ + _____ = preplanned

8. _____ + _____ = wreckage

Lesson 67

Part A

1. _____   5. _____

2. _____   6. _____

3. _____   7. _____

4. _____   8. _____

Part B

1. _____

2. _____

Part C

Add these morphographs together.
Some of the words follow the rule about doubling the final **c** in short words.

1. play + ful   = _____

2. re + source   = _____

3. spin + ing   = _____

4. style + ish   = _____

5. wrap + er   = _____

6. straight + en + ing = _____

7. re + store   = _____

8. sad + est   = _____

Part D

These words are in the puzzle.
Circle 7 or more of the words.

serving	line	port
berry	plan	voice
sign	game	vote
arm	sell	equal

```
s g i s i g n
s e r v i n g
b q l p o o a
e u v l o t m
r a o a a r e
r l i n e r t
y v o i c e m
```

Lesson 68

Part A

1. study
2. pity
3. copy
4. fancy
5. sturdy
6. hurry
7. busy
8. worry
9. story
10. carry
11. glory
12. fury

Part B

1. _____

2. _____

Part C

1. _____
2. _____
3. _____

4. _____
5. _____
6. _____

Part D

Write the word for each meaning.
The words will contain these morphographs:

ish — like   **de** — away from, down

al — related to   **ful** — full of

en — to make   **pre** — before

word	**meaning**
1. _____	full of hope
2. _____	to make wide
3. _____	press down
4. _____	like a child
5. _____	plan before
6. _____	related to rent

Part E

Fill in the blanks to show the morphographs in each word.

1. _____ + _____ + _____ = resourceful
2. _____ + _____ = wrapping
3. _____ + _____ = straightest
4. _____ + _____ + _____ = designer
5. _____ + _____ + _____ = reserving
6. _____ + _____ = stopping
7. _____ + _____ = noting
8. _____ + _____ = notable
9. _____ + _____ = used
10. _____ + _____ + _____ = strengthening

Lesson 69

Part A

1. __ o __ __ __ __   5. __ __ __ __ __ y

2. __ u __ __   6. __ u s __

3. __ u r __ __   7. __ __ __ __ __ __

4. __ __ __ c __ __   8. __ __ __ __ __ __

Part B

Please answer the question.

_____

Part C

Part D

Make 11 real words from the morphographs in the box.

fine   wide   ly   est   bare   quiet   ness

1. _____   7. _____

2. _____   8. _____

3. _____   9. _____

4. _____   10. _____

5. _____   11. _____

6. _____

Lesson 70

Part A

date	plate
fate	state
hate	rate
late	skate

Part B

___ e a s __   ___ w e _   ___ ___   q u ___ t i o__.

_____

Part C

Add these morphographs together.
Remember, the morphograph **y** is a vowel letter.

1. shine + y = _____   5. spot + y = _____

2. sleep + y = _____   6. ease + y = _____

3. noise + y = _____   7. dress + y = _____

4. length + y = _____   8. scare + y = _____

Part D

Circle the misspelled word in each group.
Then write it correctly in the blank.

1. madnes	2. design	3. heard
story	reserve	people
picture	saddness	noise
chalk	sturdy	rong

_____   _____   _____

4. quietly	5. studey	6. several
equally	straight	packege
really	stretch	final
proove	strength	bridge

_____   _____   _____

Lesson 71

Part A

_ _ _ a s _   _ _ _ w _ _   _ _ _   q _ _ _ _ t _ i _ .

_____

Part B

1. _____   5. _____

2. _____   6. _____

3. _____   7. _____

4. _____   8. _____

Part C

Part D

Add these morphographs together.
Remember, the morphograph **y** is a vowel letter.

1. ease + y   = _____
2. fool + ish + ly   = _____
3. form + al + ly   = _____
4. store + age   = _____
5. sleep + y   = _____
6. length + y   = _____
7. fate + al   = _____
8. re + source + ful = _____
9. note + able   = _____
10. straight + en   = _____

Part E

Fill in the blanks to show the morphographs in each word.

1. _____ + _____ + _____ = designer
2. _____ + _____ + _____ = unplanned
3. _____ + _____ + _____ = strengthening
4. _____ + _____ = maddest
5. _____ + _____ + _____ = related
6. _____ + _____ = wreckage
7. _____ + _____ = really
8. _____ + _____ + _____ = unproven

Lesson 72

Part A

1. _____

2. _____

3. _____

4. _____

5. _____

6. _____

Part B

_ _ _ _ _ _ _   _ _ _ _ _ _   _ _ _   _ _ _ _ _ _ _ _ _ .

_____

Part C

Part D

people	study	searching	misquoted
reviewed	heard	shoes	wreckage
hopefully	wander	teacher	straight
person	resource	stopping	carry
reserve	prove	stretcher	clothes
nerve	please	wrote	equally

Part E

Add these morphographs together.
Remember to use your spelling rules.

1. state + ly   = _____

2. step + ing   = _____

3. spot + less   = _____

4. safe + ly   = _____

5. style + ish   = _____

6. store + age   = _____

7. de + serve + ed   = _____

8. re + fine + ed   = _____

9. win + er   = _____

10. un + plan + ed   = _____

Lesson 73

Part A

1. _____

2. _____

Part B

answer	notable	equally	caught
style	really	straight	cloudy
fancy	faultless	resource	thoughtless
lately	fired	heard	mistaken
together	misjudged	wreckage	people
graceful	question	misquoted	clothes

Part C

Circle each short word that ends **cvc.**
Remember: short words have four letters or less
y is a vowel letter at the end of a morphograph.

1. trip   5. fury   9. pass

2. joy   6. pray   10. shop

3. wander   7. drop   11. tray

4. step   8. swim   12. hit

Part D

Cross out the misspelled words in these sentences.
Then write the words correctly above the crossed-out words.

I like to wandor thrugh the woulds.

The speeker missquoted his sorce.

Part E

These words are in the puzzle.
Circle 7 or more of the words.

strength	hate	rent
stretch	rest	best
swim	mash	wash
sack	hot	catch

s h o t m s b c
s t r c h a e h
w a r e s t s t
s t r e n g t h
w a s h t t s a
i i c a t c h t
m m i k s s h e

Lesson 74

Part A

1. _____   4. _____

2. _____   5. _____

3. _____

Part B

1. _____	15. _____	29. _____
2. _____	16. _____	30. _____
3. _____	17. _____	31. _____
4. _____	18. _____	32. _____
5. _____	19. _____	33. _____
6. _____	20. _____	34. _____
7. _____	21. _____	35. _____
8. _____	22. _____	36. _____
9. _____	23. _____	37. _____
10. _____	24. _____	38. _____
11. _____	25. _____	39. _____
12. _____	26. _____	40. _____
13. _____	27. _____	
14. _____	28. _____	

Part C

Draw a line from each word to its clue.

vary •   • a story

whole •   • We'll fill the _____ with dirt.

hear •   • Someone stepped on the cat's _____ .

hole •   • Have you read the _____ book?

here •   • correct

tail •   • change something

tale •   • _____ story do you like?

which •   • Winning that race was quite a _____ .

feat •   • I don't _____ any noise.

right •   • They left their coats _____ .

Lesson 75

Part A

1. _____

2. _____

Part B

1. _____   4. _____

2. _____   5. _____

3. _____   6. _____

Part C

Make 11 real words from the morphographs in the box.

ed	er	rent	bare	ing	serve	dine

1. _____   7. _____

2. _____   8. _____

3. _____   9. _____

4. _____   10. _____

5. _____   11. _____

6. _____

Part D

Fill in the blanks to show the morphographs in each word.

1. _____ + _____ = shopping

2. _____ + _____ = widely

3. _____ + _____ = hopeless

4. _____ + _____ = hoping

5. _____ + _____ = runner

6. _____ + _____ = cared

Lesson 76

Part A

consonant-y + anything, except i

1. study + ed   = _____

2. happy + ness = _____

3. play + er   = _____

4. copy + ing   = _____

5. pity + ful   = _____

6. deny + ed   = _____

Part B

1. _____   5. _____

2. _____   6. _____

3. _____   7. _____

4. _____   8. _____

Part C

Make 15 real words from the morphographs in the box.

hope	use	ful	less	ly	care	rest

1. _____   9. _____

2. _____   10. _____

3. _____   11. _____

4. _____   12. _____

5. _____   13. _____

6. _____   14. _____

7. _____   15. _____

8. _____

Part D

Add these morphographs together.
Some of the words follow the rule about doubling the final **c** in short words.

1. big + est   = _____

2. shop + ing   = _____

3. sad + en   = _____

4. deal + er   = _____

5. run + ing   = _____

6. mad + ness   = _____

7. strength + en = _____

8. form + al + ly = _____

Lesson 77

Part A

1. _____   4. _____

2. _____   5. _____

3. _____   6. _____

Part B

consonant-y + anything, except i

1. sturdy + ness = _____

2. dry + ing   = _____

3. worry + ed   = _____

4. fancy + ful   = _____

5. play + ful   = _____

6. hurry + ing   = _____

94

Part C

Part D

Add these morphographs together.

1. style + ish = _____
2. store + age = _____
3. fine + al + ly = _____
4. re + mark + able = _____
5. un + pre + serve + ed = _____
6. mis + take + en = _____
7. de + light + ed = _____
8. gold + en = _____
9. harm + less + ly = _____
10. pre + view + ed = _____
11. quiet + est = _____
12. noise + y = _____
13. pre + date + ed = _____
14. sad + en = _____

Lesson 78

Part A

        tax   box   fox

Part B

1. _____

2. _____

Part C

Write **s** or **es** in the second column.
Then add the morphographs together.

        s or **es**

1. press + _____ = _____

2. shop   + _____ = _____

3. dish   + _____ = _____

4. stretch + _____ = _____

5. goat   + _____ = _____

6. glass + _____ = _____

Part D

    consonant-y + anything, except i

Add the morphographs together.
Some of the words follow the rule about changing **y** to **i** in a word.

1. copy + ing   = _____

2. sturdy + er   = _____

3. cry + er   = _____

4. dry + ed   = _____

5. stay + ed   = _____

6. sturdy + ness = _____

Part E

Fill in the blanks to show the morphographs in each word.

1. _____ + _____ + _____ = informal

2. _____ + _____ = disease

3. _____ + _____ = easy

4. _____ + _____ = dropping

5. _____ + _____ = package

6. _____ + _____ + _____ = formally

7. _____ + _____ = hopeless

8. _____ + _____ = hoping

Lesson 79

Part A

consonant·y + anything, except i

Add the morphographs together.
Some of the words follow the rule about changing **y** to **i** in a word.

1. pity + ful = _____

2. carry + ed = _____

3. fancy + est = _____

4. like + ly + est = _____

5. try + ing = _____

6. friend + ly + ness = _____

7. study + ing = _____

8. play + ful = _____

Part B

1. _____   4. _____

2. _____   5. _____

3. _____   6. _____

Part C

Part D

Write **s** or **es** in the second column.
Then add the morphographs together.

s or es

1. witch + _____ = _____

2. tail + _____ = _____

3. pinch + _____ = _____

4. mess + _____ = _____

5. lunch + _____ = _____

6. glass + _____ = _____

7. farm + _____ = _____

8. bush + _____ = _____

Lesson 80

Part A

consonant·y + anything, except i

Add the morphographs together.
Some of the words follow the rule about changing **y** to **i** in a word.

1. happy + ness   = _____

2. stay + ed   = _____

3. try + ed   = _____

4. dry + ing   = _____

5. deny + al   = _____

6. hurry + ed   = _____

7. vary + ed   = _____

8. un + like + ly + ness = _____

Part B

Make 14 real words from the morphographs in the box.

de	er	fine	serve	light	ing	grade

1. _____   8. _____

2. _____   9. _____

3. _____   10. _____

4. _____   11. _____

5. _____   12. _____

6. _____   13. _____

7. _____   14. _____

Part C

Draw a line from each word to its clue.

whole •　　　• That door has a _____ in it.

vary •　　　• Would you come _____ , please?

here •　　　• They wrote a _____ book.

hole •　　　• a story

tale •　　　• change

very •　　　• The play made me feel _____ sad.

Part D

Add these morphographs together.

1. con + strict = _____

2. re + in + state = _____

3. stitch + es = _____

4. worth + y = _____

5. store + age = _____

6. child + ish + ly = _____

7. luck + y = _____

8. con + form + ing = _____

9. fine + al + ly = _____

10. in + human = _____

Lesson 81

Part A

leave　　neat　　main　　claim

Part B

Whose turn is it to move?

_____

Part C

Add the morphographs together.
Some of the words follow the rule
about changing the **y** to **i** in a word.

1. vary + ed = _____
2. happy + est = _____
3. spray + ed = _____
4. friend+ly+ness = _____
5. worry + ing = _____
6. carry + ed = _____

Part D

Write **s** or **es** in the second column.
Then add the morphographs together.

s or es

1. bench + _____ = _____
2. reach + _____ = _____
3. box + _____ = _____
4. wash + _____ = _____
5. claim + _____ = _____
6. mess + _____ = _____

Part E

Circle the misspelled word in each group.
Then write it correctly on the line.

1. world
   cought
   shining
   wander
   _____

2. happy
   motor
   auther
   friend
   _____

3. stretch
   choice
   herb
   larje
   _____

4. equil
   change
   hopeful
   trace
   _____

5. depressing
   quiut
   human
   wrong
   _____

6. should
   would
   could
   noize
   _____

Lesson 82

Part A

1. _____   4. _____

2. _____   5. _____

3. _____   6. _____

Part B

W h o s e __ u r __ __ __ __ __ __ __ __ o __ e ?

_____

Part C

Add the morphographs together.
Some of the words follow the rule about changing **y** to **i** in a word.

1. happy + ly   = _____

2. con + fine   = _____

3. in + side   = _____

4. girl + ish + ness   = _____

5. pity + ed   = _____

6. un + claim + ed   = _____

7. neat + ly   = _____

8. like + ly + ness   = _____

9. rain + y   = _____

10. store + age   = _____

11. norm + al + ly   = _____

12. un + drink + able = _____

13. play + ful   = _____

14. de + press + ing   = _____

15. worry + ed   = _____

Part D

Fill in the blanks to show the morphographs in each word

1. _____ + _____ = civilly

2. _____ + _____ + _____ = strengthening

3. _____ + _____ + _____ = informer

4. _____ + _____ = really

5. _____ + _____ = planning

6. _____ + _____ = changing

7. _____ + _____ + _____ = formally

8. _____ + _____ = wreckage

9. _____ + _____ + _____ = preplanned

10. _____ + _____ + _____ = hopefully

Lesson 83

Part A

___ ___ ___ s e ___u___ ___ ___ ___ ___ ___ ___ ___o___ ___ ?

_____

Part B

1. _____ + _____ = _____

2. _____ + _____ = _____

3. _____ + _____ = _____

4. _____ + _____ = _____

5. _____ + _____ = _____

6. _____ + _____ = _____

Part C

1. _____

2. _____

Part D

Draw a line from each word to its clue.

lone   •   • change

vary   •   • putting words on paper

write   •   • I can _____ the music.

which   •   • by yourself

tail   •   • all parts together

hear   •   • I _____ the answer.

whole   •   • the end of something

know   •   • _____ style do you like?

Part E

Write **s** or **es** in the second column.
Then add the morphographs together.

s or **es**

1. patch   + _____ = _____

2. box   + _____ = _____

3. claim   + _____ = _____

4. class   + _____ = _____

5. reach   + _____ = _____

6. sign   + _____ = _____

7. witch   + _____ = _____

8. speech + _____ = _____

Lesson 84

Part A

1. _____   4. _____

2. _____   5. _____

3. _____   6. _____

Part B

1. _____

2. _____

Part C

Figure out the rule and write it. Remember to spell the words correctly.

and the next morphograph begins with **v** . . . when the word ends **cvc** . . . Double the final **c** in a short word

_____

_____

Part D

misquoted	wrote	valuable	replace
heard	unproven	leave	maddest
ground	equally	package	touching
confuse	straighten	sturdy	trail
defined	different	cloudy	research
failing	resourceful	unequal	inhuman

Part E

Circle the misspelled word in each group.
Then write it correctly on the line.

1. brother	2. rong	3. shineing
story	wrap	hurried
shuld	fancy	joyful
were	civil	wander
_____	_____	_____

4. stretch	5. swimer	6. stretcher
civilly	runner	friendly
realy	story	unarmmed
unfilling	restful	shopper
_____	_____	_____

Lesson 85

Part A

1. _ _ _ _ i _ _

2. _ _ _ _ _ g h _

3. _ _ i _ _ _ _ _

4. _ r _ _ _ a _ _

5. _ _ _ _ i _ _

6. _ _ o _ _

Part B

1. _____

2. _____

3. _____

4. _____

5. _____

6. _____

Part C

Figure out the rules and write them. Remember to spell the words correctly.

1. a word when the next morphograph begins . . . Drop the **e** from . . . with a vowel letter

   _____

   _____

2. **cvc** and the next . . . Double the final **c** . . . morphograph begins with **v** . . . in a short word when the word ends

   _____

   _____

Part D

wander	informer	research
rebuild	stretcher	inhuman
neatly	confine	touching
claim	quietly	turn
person	moving	replace
whose	preschool	maddest
cheapest	delightful	cloudy

Part E

Circle each short word that ends **cvc**.
Remember: The letter **x** acts like two consonant letters.

1. stop	4. mad	7. rent	10. box	13. boy
2. brother	5. play	8. hot	11. star	14. water
3. fox	6. buzz	9. bar	12. bare	15. snap

Part F

Add the morphographs together.
Some of the words follow the rule about dropping an **e**.

1. write + ing = _____

2. in + value + able = _____

3. late + ly = _____

4. lone + ly = _____

5. force + ful + ly = _____

6. note + able = _____

7. change + ing = _____

8. re + serve + ed = _____

Lesson 86

Part A

1. _____

2. _____

Part B

1. _____ + _____ = _____

2. _____ + _____ = _____

3. _____ + _____ = _____

4. _____ + _____ = _____

5. _____ + _____ = _____

6. _____ + _____ = _____

Part C

1. _____	15. _____	29. _____
2. _____	16. _____	30. _____
3. _____	17. _____	31. _____
4. _____	18. _____	32. _____
5. _____	19. _____	33. _____
6. _____	20. _____	34. _____
7. _____	21. _____	35. _____
8. _____	22. _____	36. _____
9. _____	23. _____	37. _____
10. _____	24. _____	38. _____
11. _____	25. _____	39. _____
12. _____	26. _____	40. _____
13. _____	27. _____	
14. _____	28. _____	

Part D

Make 11 real words from the morphographs in the box.

fine	re	sign	serve	de	con	form

1. _____   7. _____
2. _____   8. _____
3. _____   9. _____
4. _____   10. _____
5. _____   11. _____
6. _____

Part E

Fill in the blanks to show the morphographs in each word.

1. _____ + _____ + _____ = remaining

2. _____ + _____ + _____ = foolishly

3. _____ + _____ = lonely

4. _____ + _____ = rainy

5. _____ + _____ + _____ + _____ = uninformed

6. _____ + _____ = conform

7. _____ + _____ + _____ = related

8. _____ + _____ = voltage

Lesson 87

Part A

show   grow   low   flow   throw   blow   know

Part B

1. _____   5. _____

2. _____   6. _____

3. _____   7. _____

4. _____   8. _____

Part C

1. _____ + _____ = _____

2. _____ + _____ = _____

3. _____ + _____ = _____

4. _____ + _____ = _____

5. _____ + _____ = _____

6. _____ + _____ = _____

Part D

Part E

Figure out the rules and write them.

1. word ends **cvc** and . . . Double the final **c** in . . . the next morphograph
   begins with **v** . . . a short word when the

2. word when the next . . . a vowel letter . . . morphograph begins with . . .
   Drop the **e** from a

Lesson 88

Part A

1. _____

2. _____

Part B

1. _____ + _____ = _____

2. _____ + _____ = _____

3. _____ + _____ = _____

4. _____ + _____ = _____

5. _____ + _____ = _____

6. _____ + _____ = _____

Part C

These words are in the puzzle.
Circle 7 or more of the words.

denied	patch	date
runner	ease	madder
nail	painter	stored
feel	dented	deny

```
r d d e n y s
n u e a s e t
n a n n t e o
p a i n t e r
f e e l e e e
m a d d e r d
d a p a t c h
```

Part D

Add the morphographs together.

1. un + claim + ed = _____

2. slam + ed = _____

3. con + fine + ing = _____

4. in + still + ed = _____

5. re + act + ing = _____

6. style + ish + ly = _____

7. con + fuse + ing = _____

8. un + luck + y = _____

9. fine + al = _____

10. in + flame + ing = _____

11. leak + age = _____

12. un + read + able = _____

Lesson 89

Part A

spray   text   tract   ruin   fluid

Part B

1. __ __ o w
2. __ __ r __ w
3. __ __ __ __ __
4. __ __ __ __ __
5. k __ __ __ __
6. __ l __ __ __

Part C

1. _____
2. _____

Part D

snugness	unbreakable	equally	floating
research	confuse	friendly	storage
deserve	misspelling	stepping	insure

Part E

Cross out the misspelled words in these sentences.
Then write the words correctly above the crossed-out words.

Pleaze open your books to page ate.

There is a valueable packege in the trunk.

Part F
Fill in the blanks to show the morphographs in each word.

1. _____ + _____ + _____ + _____ = undefeated

2. _____ + _____ + _____ = confirmed

3. _____ + _____ = moving

4. _____ + _____ + _____ = removal

5. _____ + _____ = contract

6. _____ + _____ = context

7. _____ + _____ + _____ = instated

8. _____ + _____ = sleepy

9. _____ + _____ = dosage

10. _____ + _____ + _____ = fatally

Lesson 90

Part A

1. _____

2. _____

Part B

Draw a line from each word to its clue.

loan •   • doing something great

weather •   • by yourself

lone •   • putting words on paper

feat •   • I will _____ you my shirt.

whole •   • We can't _____ your voice.

hear •   • correct

whether •   • The _____ is good today.

write •   • a story

tale •   • Do you know _____ you will go?

right •   • I ate a _____ cake.

Part C

Figure out the rules and write them.

1. a word when the next . . . vowel letter . . . Drop the **e** from . . . morphograph begins with a

_____

_____

2. next morphograph begins with **v** . . . the word ends **cvc** and the . . . **c** in a short word when . . . Double the final

_____

_____

Part D

Add the morphographs together.

1. glass + es = _____
2. race + s = _____
3. re + tract = _____
4. flat + est = _____
5. note + able = _____
6. in + cure + able = _____
7. con + fine + ing = _____
8. wreck + age = _____
9. globe + al = _____
10. con + test = _____

Lesson 91

Part A

1. _ _ _ _ _ y   3. _ _ _ _ c t   5. _ _ _ _ i _

2. _ _ _ _ _   4. _ u _ _

Part B

1. _____
2. _____
3. _____

4. _____
5. _____
6. _____

Part C

1. _____ + _____ = _____
2. _____ + _____ = _____
3. _____ + _____ = _____
4. _____ + _____ = _____
5. _____ + _____ = _____
6. _____ + _____ = _____

Part D

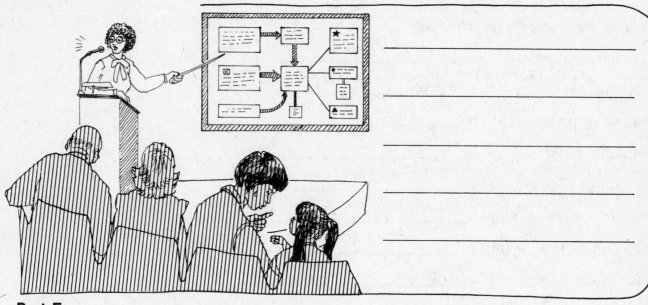

Part E

Fill in the circle marked **R** if the underlined word is spelled right.
Fill in the circle marked **W** if the underlined word is spelled wrong.

1. We have had very bad <u>weather</u> lately.   Ⓡ   Ⓦ

2. Are you <u>planing</u> a party?   Ⓡ   Ⓦ

3. That was a <u>realy</u> funny story.   Ⓡ   Ⓦ

4. I <u>believe</u> we won the race.   Ⓡ   Ⓦ

5. My sister <u>wrote</u> me a long note.   Ⓡ   Ⓦ

6. Have you <u>studyed</u> for the test?   Ⓡ   Ⓦ

Lesson 92

Part A

Our yellow flowers bloomed early.

_____

Part B

1. _____ + _____ = _____
2. _____ + _____ = _____
3. _____ + _____ = _____
4. _____ + _____ = _____
5. _____ + _____ = _____
6. _____ + _____ = _____

Part C

Add the morphographs together.

1. con + text = _____
2. ruin + ed = _____
3. con + tract = _____
4. lone + ly = _____
5. un + de + feat + ed = _____
6. fine + al + ly = _____
7. person + al + ly = _____
8. watch + es = _____
9. noise + y = _____
10. trail + er = _____

Part D

These words are in the puzzle.
Circle 7 or more of the words.

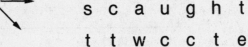

throw	error	threw
house	large	worry
reach	storage	teach
caught	cure	eight

```
s c a u g h t
t t w c c t e
e h o u s e a
i r r r r r c
g o r e a c h
h w y o w g a
t t l a r g e
```

Lesson 93

Part A

cause   pause   poison   strange

Part B

1. _____   4. _____

2. _____   5. _____

3. _____   6. _____

Part C

O u __   y e __ l __ w   __ __ o w __ __ __

__ __ o o __ e __   e a r __ __ __ .

_____

Part D

1. _____   4. _____

2. _____   5. _____

3. _____   6. _____

Part E

Add the morphographs together.
Some of the words follow the rule about changing the **y** to **i** in a word.

1. worry + ed   = _____

2. pity + ful   = _____

3. study + ing   = _____

4. play + ful + ly   = _____

5. boy + ish + ness   = _____

6. try + ed   = _____

7. hurry + ing   = _____

8. fancy + ful   = _____

Lesson 94

Part A

1. _____

2. _____

Part B

1. __ __ u __ __ __ __

2. __ a __ s __

3. __ __ __ u g __ __

4. __ o __ __ o

5. __ a __ __ __

6. __ __ r __ n g __

Part C

__ u __   y __ __ __ w   __ __ o w __ __ __

__ __ __ o __   e a __ __ __ .

_____

Part D

Part E

Fill in the blanks to show the morphographs in each word.

1. _____ + _____ = strangely

2. _____ + _____ = consent

3. _____ + _____ + _____ = presented

4. _____ + _____ + _____ = misplaced

5. _____ + _____ + _____ = winners

6. _____ + _____ + _____ = invaluable

7. _____ + _____ = wonderful

8. _____ + _____ + _____ = reserved

Lesson 95

Part A

_ _ _   y _ _ _ _ _ _   _ _ _ w _ _ _

_ _ _ _ _ _ _ _   _ _ a _ _ _ .

_____

Part B

1. _____

2. _____

3. _____

4. _____

5. _____

6. _____

Part C

Draw a line from each word to its clue.

weather •   • by yourself

loan •   • ordinary

plain •   • Let's decide _____ or not we will go.

right •   • Today's _____ is fine.

lone •   • change

whether •   • Please _____ me some paint.

vary •   • I have a _____ in my shoe.

hole •   • You gave the _____ answer.

Part D

Add the morphographs together.
Remember to use your spelling rules.

1. early + est   = _____

2. con + fine + ment = _____

3. happy + est   = _____

4. cloud + y + ness   = _____

5. scratch + es   = _____

6. pay + ment   = _____

7. dark + ness   = _____

8. strange + est   = _____

9. tough + est   = _____

10. grace + ful + ly = _____

Lesson 96

Part A

1. brain	3. drain	5. plain	7. sprain
2. chain	4. gain	6. rain	8. stain

Part B

1. _____

2. _____

Part C

1. _____   4. _____

2. _____   5. _____

3. _____   6. _____

Part D

speaker	delightful	preview	sprayed	early
straightest	greatness	resourceful	statement	quotable
really	informal	patches	flower	pleasing
stain	wonderful	mistaken	ruined	contract
storage	leader	lunches	shopping	strange

Part E

Circle the misspelled word in each group.
Then write it correctly on the line.

1. cloudy	2. stranger	3. flowers	4. lenghten
contract	driping	yello	package
pichure	whose	pause	movement
question	leader	regain	caught

_____   _____   _____   _____

5. relate	6. through	7. misspelled	8. cawze
wonderful	eight	ruined	valuable
poisen	people	equaly	resources
speaker	helplesness	mistake	confused

_____   _____   _____   _____

Lesson 97

Part A

Part B

Part C

spotted	boxes	pause	rainy	straightest
quotable	happiness	yellow	contract	wonderful
throat	cheapest	trail	cause	ruined
together	graceful	speeches	early	resourceful
pleasing	studying	blowing	strange	speaker

Part D

Fill in the blanks to show the morphographs in each word.

1. _____ + _____ + _____ = department
2. _____ + _____ + _____ = confinement
3. _____ + _____ + _____ + _____ = unconfirmed
4. _____ + _____ + _____ = investment
5. _____ + _____ = lucky
6. _____ + _____ = voltage
7. _____ + _____ + _____ = normally
8. _____ + _____ = valuable
9. _____ + _____ + _____ = delightful

Lesson 98

Part A

1. _____   15. _____   29. _____
2. _____   16. _____   30. _____
3. _____   17. _____   31. _____
4. _____   18. _____   32. _____
5. _____   19. _____   33. _____
6. _____   20. _____   34. _____
7. _____   21. _____   35. _____
8. _____   22. _____   36. _____
9. _____   23. _____   37. _____
10. _____   24. _____   38. _____
11. _____   25. _____   39. _____
12. _____   26. _____   40. _____
13. _____   27. _____
14. _____   28. _____

Part B

1. _____

2. _____

Part C

Figure out the rules and write them.

1. in a word when the . . . next morphograph begins with . . . word ends
consonant-and-y and the . . . Change the **y** to **i** . . . anything, except **i**

_____

_____

2. with a **v** . . . morphograph begins . . . word when the next . . . Drop the **e** from a

_____

_____

Lesson 99

Part A

1. _____   4. _____

2. _____   5. _____

3. _____   6. _____

Part B

124

Part C

Make 10 real words from the morphographs in the box.

| en | est | sad | mad | ness | wide | fine |

1. _____
2. _____
3. _____
4. _____
5. _____

6. _____
7. _____
8. _____
9. _____
10. _____

Part D

Fill in the blanks to show the morphographs in each word.

1. _____ + _____ = stranger
2. _____ + _____ = taken
3. _____ + _____ = choicest
4. _____ + _____ = forceful
5. _____ + _____ = signal
6. _____ + _____ + _____ = resigned
7. _____ + _____ + _____ = contracted
8. _____ + _____ + _____ = consignment
9. _____ + _____ + _____ + _____ = unmistakable
10. _____ + _____ + _____ = wonderfully

Lesson 100

Part A

1. _____
2. _____

Part B

Make 15 real words from the morphographs in the box.

| fine | con | de | re | ment | move | ing | ed |

1. _____   9. _____
2. _____   10. _____
3. _____   11. _____
4. _____   12. _____
5. _____   13. _____
6. _____   14. _____
7. _____   15. _____
8. _____

Part C

These words are in the puzzle.
Circle 7 or more of the words.

civil   verb   carry
might   deny   robber
gone   dine   match
mad   does   easy

```
c i v i l r
m a d e r o
a i r i r b
t d g r n b
c e o h y e
h n n e t r
m y e a s y
```

Part D

Add the morphographs together.
Some of the words follow the rule about changing y to i in a word.

1. boy + ish   = _____   6. carry + er = _____
2. sturdy + ness = _____   7. cry + ing = _____
3. worry + ed   = _____   8. try + al   = _____
4. pity + ful   = _____   9. deny + al = _____
5. sign + al   = _____   10. fly + er = _____

Lesson 101

Part A

Write contractions for the words in the first column.

1. could not = _____   5. he will   = _____

2. should not = _____   6. would not = _____

3. she is   = _____   7. I have   = _____

4. is not   = _____   8. you will = _____

Part B

1. _____   4. _____

2. _____   5. _____

3. _____   6. _____

Part C

Carrying the heavy load is sure to make me breathe hard.

_____

_____

Part D

Circle the misspelled word in each group.
Then write it correctly on the line.

1. other	2. story	3. yellow	4. author
wonderfull	mispell	strength	poison
wrong	sturdy	serve	saddness
could	fancy	strech	civil

_____   _____   _____   _____

5. dripping	6. peeple	7. valeu	8. useless
enuff	delightful	unthinking	wanted
pitch	rebuild	date	worrying
normal	while	coldest	frends

_____   _____   _____   _____

Lesson 102

Part A

Write contractions for the words in the first column.

1. were not = _____   5. you have = _____

2. does not = _____   6. did not = _____

3. are not = _____   7. can not = _____

4. she will = _____   8. they are = _____

Part B

__ a __ r y ___ ___   ___ ___ ___   __ e a __ y   __ o a __   __ __

s __ u r __   __ __   __ __ k __   __ __   __ __ e a __ __ e   __ a __ __ __.

_____

_____

Part C

Make 10 real words from the morphographs in the box.

pity	er	ed	fancy	ful	ing	play

1. _____   6. _____

2. _____   7. _____

3. _____   8. _____

4. _____   9. _____

5. _____   10. _____

Part D

Add the morphographs together.

1. catch + es   = _____

2. mis + print + ed   = _____

3. un + snap + ed   = _____

4. point + less   = _____

5. re + serve + ed   = _____

6. fit + ness   = _____

7. de + light + ful   = _____

8. un + de + feat + ed = _____

9. un + vary + ed   = _____

10. leak + age   = _____

11. speed + y + est   = _____

12. ship + ment   = _____

13. in + tend + ed   = _____

14. con + front   = _____

Lesson 103

Part A

1. _____

2. _____

Part B

__ a __ __ y __ __   ___ __ __   __ e a __ __   ____ __   __ __

__ u r __   __ __   _____   __ __   __ __ e a __ __ e   ____.

_____

_____

Part C

Write the word for each meaning.
The words will contain these morphographs.

al — related to   **ful** — full of   **est** — the most

pre — before   **ish** — like   **en** — make

1. _____   like a baby

2. _____   the most late

3. _____   related to signs

4. _____   wrap before

5. _____   make light

6. _____   full of care

Part D

Write contractions for the words in the first column.

1. let us   = _____   5. we have   = _____

2. have not = _____   6. what is   = _____

3. was not = _____   7. he is   = _____

4. they will = _____   8. would not = _____

Part E

Add the morphographs together.

1. swim + er   = _____

2. fine + est   = _____

3. wide + est   = _____

4. con + sign   = _____

5. mad + ly   = _____

6. rage + ing   = _____

7. trap + er   = _____

8. un + civil + ly = _____

Lesson 104

Part A

_____ ___ __a__ _____ __

____ __ ____ __ _____e _____.

_____

_____

Part B

Complete each sentence correctly with one of these words:

write   right

1. My grandmother likes it when I _____ long letters.

2. Janis is the _____ person for the job.

3. My answers on the test were all _____ .

4. When Martin was four years old, he could _____ his name.

Part C

Write the contractions for the words in the first column.

1. has not = _____   5. I will   = _____

2. you are = _____   6. they are = _____

3. we will = _____   7. were not = _____

4. are not = _____   8. it is   = _____

Part D

Circle the misspelled word in each group.
Then write it correctly on the line.

1. worry	2. catch	3. hurring	4. claim
might	friend	fitness	queit
brother	wandor	preview	choice
civel	change	ruined	equal

_____ _____ _____ _____

Part E

Fill in the blanks to show the morphographs in each word.

1. _____ + _____ + _____ +_____ = unrefined

2. _____ + _____ + _____ = packaging

3. _____ + _____ + _____ = rightfully

4. _____ + _____ = inhuman

5. _____ + _____ + _____ = strengthening

6. _____ + _____ + _____ = loneliness

7. _____ + _____ + _____ = helplessness

8. _____ + _____ + _____ = unequally

9. _____ + _____ + _____ = resigned

10. _____ + _____ + _____ +_____ = unrelated

Lesson 105

Part A

1. _____

_____

2. _____

Part B

1. _____   5. _____

2. _____   6. _____

3. _____   7. _____

4. _____   8. _____

Part C

Write the contractions for the words in the first column.

1. should not = _____   4. what is = _____

2. she is   = _____   5. they will = _____

3. I have   = _____   6. we are   = _____

Part D

Complete each sentence correctly with one of these words:

weather   which   very   sale   would

1. Are those toys for _____?

2. That rack is _____ heavy.

3. The _____ has been cold and rainy all week.

4. Do you know _____ answer is correct?

5. I _____ stay longer if I had more time.

6. Our spelling test was _____ easy.

Part E

Figure out the rules and write them.

1. in a short word then the . . . next morphograph begins with **v** . . .
   Double the final **c** . . . word ends **cvc** and the

   _____

   _____

2. a consonant-and-**y** and the . . . a word when the word ends with . . .
   next morphograph begins with anything, except **i** . . . Change the **y** to **i** in

   _____

   _____

Lesson 106

Part A

1. _____ + _____ = _____
2. _____ + _____ = _____
3. _____ + _____ = _____
4. _____ + _____ = _____
5. _____ + _____ = _____
6. _____ + _____ = _____
7. _____ + _____ = _____
8. _____ + _____ = _____

Part B

1. _____
2. _____

Part C

Make 11 real words from the morphographs in the box.

friend	ly	happy	ness	lone	sturdy	est

1. _____   7. _____
2. _____   8. _____
3. _____   9. _____
4. _____   10. _____
5. _____   11. _____
6. _____

Part D

Write the contractions for the words in the first column.

1. can not = _____   5. are not = _____
2. does not = _____   6. what is = _____
3. they will = _____   7. it is   = _____
4. you have = _____   8. let us = _____

Part E

Fill in the blanks to show the morphographs in each word.

1. _____ + _____ = sadder

2. _____ + _____ = strengthen

3. _____ + _____ + _____ = informal

4. _____ + _____ = useful

5. _____ + _____ = express

6. _____ + _____ + _____ = reserving

7. _____ + _____ + _____ = defacing

8. _____ + _____ = planning

Lesson 108

Part A

1. _____ + _____ = _____

2. _____ + _____ = _____

3. _____ + _____ = _____

4. _____ + _____ = _____

5. _____ + _____ = _____

6. _____ + _____ = _____

7. _____ + _____ = _____

8. _____ + _____ = _____

Part B

Part C

Add the morphographs together.

1. re + move + al = _____

2. in + come = _____

3. rise + ing = _____

4. safe + ly = _____

5. hot + est = _____

6. mad + ness = _____

7. un + de + serve + ing = _____

8. use + age = _____

9. verb + al + ly = _____

10. re + cent + ly = _____

11. swim + er = _____

12. real + ly = _____

Part D

Cross out the misspelled words in these sentences.
Then write the words correctly above the crossed-out words.

Sevral stranje birds landed togather.

We are'nt leaving the main road.

That was the greatest feet of strenght I've seen.

Lesson 109

Part A

1. _____   4. _____

2. _____   5. _____

3. _____   6. _____

Part B

1. _ _ o _ _

2. _ _ _ u _ _

3. _ _ u _ _

4. _ _ _ _ _ _

5. _ _ _ w _ _

6. _ _ _ _ _ _

Part C

These words are in the puzzle.
Circle 7 or more of the words.

brotherly	stay	report
spotted	vary	race
neat	length	traps
loud	whether	cared

```
b  r  c  l  s  n  t  l  w
r  r  n  a  o  u  u  e  h
s  e  o  n  r  u  o  n  e
s  p  o  t  t  e  d  g  t
s  o  a  y  h  n  d  t  h
s  r  a  c  e  e  e  h  e
l  t  r  a  p  s  r  a  r
v  t  a  t  o  r  t  l  t
v  a  r  y  y  r  h  h  y
```

Part D

Complete each sentence correctly with one of these words:

weather   vary   write   they're   right   whole

1. Tony's new shoes are exactly the _____ size.

2. Instead of eating the same thing all the time, you should _____ your diet.

3. My uncle was so hungry last Sunday that he ate a _____ chicken.

4. The farmers aren't worried. _____ expecting good _____.

5. Joggers don't usually run at the same speed all the time. They

   usually _____ their pace.

6. The blanks on your worksheet are where you _____ spelling words.

7. Last Friday we worked the _____ day.

Lesson 110

Part A

quick   quiz   quest

Part B

1. _____

2. _____

Part C

1. _____   5. _____

2. _____   6. _____

3. _____   7. _____

4. _____   8. _____

Part D

Write **s** or **es** in the second column.
Then add the morphographs together.

s or **es**

1. glass   + _____ = _____

2. reach   + _____ = _____

3. sound   + _____ = _____

4. brush   + _____ = _____

5. scratch + _____ = _____

6. flower + _____ = _____

Part E

Fill in the blanks to show the morphographs in each word.

1. _____ + _____ + _____ = explained

2. _____ + _____ = resource

3. _____ + _____ = movement

4. _____ + _____ + _____ + _____ = unrelated

5. _____ + _____ + _____ + _____ = unconfirmed

6. _____ + _____ + _____ = informer

7. _____ + _____ + _____ = childishly

8. _____ + _____ + _____ = noisiness

Lesson 111

Part A

1. _ _ _ _ e _ _

2. _ u _ _ _

3. _ _ e _ _

4. _ _ _ _ t _ _

5. _ _ o _ _ _

6. _ _ _ _ c _ _

Part B

Part C

their •	• She has a _____ blue dress.
here •	• contraction of **they are**
vary •	• Can you _____ me some money?
plain •	• The students exchanged _____ papers.
sale •	• change
loan •	• The _____ has been good lately.
they're •	• My _____ were sore after the hike.
write •	• We moved _____ a year ago.
feet •	• Our car is for _____.
weather •	• I can _____ two words in Spanish.

Part D

Cross out the misspelled words in these sentences.
Then write the words correctly above the crossed-out words.

We worryed uselesly about the whether.

My frend chandges his cloze offen.

Lesson 112

Part A

One athlete finished the contest before everyone else.

_____

Part B

1. _____
2. _____
3. _____
4. _____
5. _____
6. _____

7. _____
8. _____
9. _____
10. _____
11. _____
12. _____

Part C

Write the contractions for the words in the first column.

1. it is   = _____
2. are not   = _____
3. that is   = _____
4. would not = _____

5. can not = _____
6. let us   = _____
7. you will = _____
8. we have = _____

140

Part D

Add the morphographs together.

1. re + quest = _____

2. win + er = _____

3. pity + ful = _____

4. strength + en + ing = _____

5. un + ex + plain + ed = _____

6. de + feat + ed = _____

7. re + place + ment = _____

8. con + front + ed = _____

9. nudge + ing = _____

10. star + ing = _____

11. ripe + ness = _____

12. straight + est = _____

Lesson 113

Part A

O_ e __ _ lete __ _ ish _ d ____
___ n __ st __ f _ re __ ve _ yo __ e _ se.

Part B

Part C

Make 9 real words from the morphographs in the box.

ed	form	re	in	er	con

1. _____ 6. _____

2. _____ 7. _____

3. _____ 8. _____

4. _____ 9. _____

5. _____

Part D

Figure out the rules and write them.

1. in a short word when the . . . Double the final **c** . . . morphograph begins
   with **v** . . . word ends **cvc** and the next

   _____

   _____

2. with anything, except **i** . . . and the next morphograph begins . . . when the word
   ends consonant-and-y . . . to **i** in a word . . . Change the **y**

   _____

   _____

Lesson 114

Part A

danger   beauty   sudden   cover

Part B

1. _____

2. _____

Part C

1. _____   5. _____

2. _____   6. _____

3. _____   7. _____

4. _____   8. _____

Part D

several	hurrying	valuable	greatly
childishness	clothes	confinement	review
stretcher	teacher	caught	sailboat
wrong	poison	speaker	leave
answer	breathe	question	ruined
picture	yellow	listening	slowly

Part E

Draw a line from each word to its clue.

peace   •   • by yourself

their   •   • they own something

whole   •   • a story

lone   •   • no fighting

tale   •   • My answer wasn't _____.

right   •   • We ate a _____ loaf of bread.

Lesson 116

Part A

O___ ___ete ___is___ ___

_____s_ ___ore __ery__e ___e.

_____

Part B

1. _____   5. _____

2. _____   6. _____

3. _____   7. _____

4. _____   8. _____

Part C

_____

_____

_____

_____

_____

Part D

Fill in the blanks to show the morphographs in each word.

1. _____ + _____ + _____ = confinement

2. _____ + _____ + _____ = wonderfully

3. _____ + _____ + _____ = requesting

4. _____ + _____ + _____ = unquotable

5. _____ + _____ + _____ = explained

6. _____ + _____ = stranger

7. _____ + _____ = poisoning

8. _____ + _____ = context

9. _____ + _____ + _____ = cloudiness

Lesson 117

Part A

chief   niece   grief   brief   thief

Part B

____   _____e t e   _____e_   ____

_____ _   ____o r e   __e__y___   _____.

_____

Part C

Part D

Add the morphographs together.
Remember to use your spelling rules.

1. beauty + ful   = _____
2. sudden + ly   = _____
3. peace + ful + ly   = _____
4. ex + change + ing = _____
5. in + vest + ment = _____
6. con + tact + ed   = _____
7. re + strict + ed = _____
8. noise + y   = _____
9. fine + al + ly   = _____
10. volt + age   = _____
11. grip + ing   = _____

Lesson 118

Part A

___ _____ e _ e _____ ____

_____ _____ e __ e _____ _____ .

_____

Part B

1. _ r _ e __   3. __ _ i ___   5. _ h ____

2. __ i _ c __   4. _____

Part C

Part D

Circle the misspelled word in each group.
Then write it correctly on the line.

1. worryed
   crying
   denied
   playful

2. chalky
   children
   cheepest
   changing

3. spotless
   maddness
   winner
   shopping

_____   _____   _____

4. straight
   stretch
   strenght
   switch

5. really
   filling
   nicely
   civily

6. thought
   enough
   thrugh
   question

_____   _____   _____

Lesson 119

Part A

govern   reason   type   house   first

Part B

1. _____   5. _____

2. _____   6. _____

3. _____   7. _____

4. _____   8. _____

Part C

1. _____

2. _____

Part D

Fill in the blanks to show the morphographs in each word.

1. _____ + _____ + _____ = defining

2. _____ + _____ = final

3. _____ + _____ + _____ = confinement

4. _____ + _____ + _____ = designer

5. _____ + _____ + _____ = resigned

6. _____ + _____ = signal

7. _____ + _____ + _____ + _____ = unrecoverable

8. _____ + _____ = heaviest

Part E

Circle the short **cvc** words.
Remember: short words have four letters or less.
          y is a vowel letter at the end of a morphograph.
          x acts like two consonant letters.

1. sudden   4. trip   7. grab   10. reason

2. boy   5. poison   8. spot   11. cover

3. chin   6. box   9. hid   12. flat

Lesson 120

Part A

1. __ y __ __
2. __ i __ __ __
3. __ o __ e r __

4. __ e a __ o __
5. __ __ u s __

Part B

1. _____

2. _____

Part C

1. _____
2. _____
3. _____

4. _____
5. _____
6. _____

Part D

Complete each sentence correctly with one of these words.

      peace   there   they're   piece   their

1. The boys are staying home because _____ sick.

2. Please put those books over _____, on the shelf.

3. Someone gave us each a _____ of pie.

4. I enjoy the _____ and quiet of the lake.

5. Mr. and Mrs. Sato lost _____ dog.

6. We all wrote a thank-you note on one _____ of paper.

7. Margo and Kim went fishing yesterday.

_____ going again this afternoon.

8. I went to your house, but you weren't _____ .

Lesson 121

Part A

Our second surprise was especially exciting.

_____

Part B

s or es   s or es

1. worry + _____ = _____   6. boy   + _____ = _____

2. story + _____ = _____   7. play   + _____ = _____

3. try   + _____ = _____   8. study + _____ = _____

4. joy   + _____ = _____   9. stay   + _____ = _____

5. copy + _____ = _____   10. carry + _____ = _____

Part C

Circle the misspelled word in each group.
Then write it correctly on the line.

1. proud	2. wander	3. auther
strength	equil	hurry
mispelled	answer	sturdy
wrong	friendly	reason
_____	_____	_____

4. pleaze	5. danger	6. rezerve
straight	should	house
whose	happiness	swimmer
niece	realy	chief
_____	_____	_____

Lesson 122

Part A

```
___   __c o   d   _u r _ i s e   ___
e __ e c i a l __   _x c _ t _ n g.
```

_____

Part B

	s or **es**			**s** or **es**
1. stay + _____ = _____		5. worry + _____ = _____
2. copy + _____ = _____		6. fly + _____ = _____
3. toy + _____ = _____		7. boy + _____ = _____
4. spray + _____ = _____		8. carry + _____ = _____

Part C

Fill in the blanks to show the morphographs in each word.

1. _____ + _____ + _____ = prolonged

2. _____ + _____ = express

3. _____ + _____ + _____ = profoundly

4. _____ + _____ + _____ = refinement

5. _____ + _____ + _____ = exported

6. _____ + _____ = conserve

7. _____ + _____ + _____ + _____ = unrelated

8. _____ + _____ = briefly

Part D

Add the morphographs together.

1. govern + ment = _____   6. un + type + ed = _____

2. rise + ing = _____   7. carry + ed = _____

3. trap + ed = _____   8. strength + en = _____

4. straight + en = _____   9. force + ful = _____

5. reason + able = _____   10. beauty + ful + ly = _____

Lesson 123

Part A

___ ____o_ ___r___s_ ____

_____c i a___ _x c_____.

Part B

	s or es				s or es	
1. boy	+ _____	= _____		5. baby	+ _____	= _____
2. story	+ _____	= _____		6. fly	+ _____	= _____
3. try	+ _____	= _____		7. study	+ _____	= _____
4. worry	+ _____	= _____		8. carry	+ _____	= _____

Part C

shouldn't	caught	replacement	chiefly
together	believe	answer	house
different	exchange	govern	greatest
children	safely	person	signal
watching	conserve	school	hurried

Part D

Complete each sentence correctly with one of these words:

would   write   they're   whole   their   very   vary   right   hole

1. Parachute jumping is a _____ exciting sport.

2. Whenever you misspell a word, you should _____ that word correctly at least

   one time.

3. A woodpecker made a small _____ in the side of our barn.

4. The boys are late because _____ helping Mrs. Olmsted.

5. No one thought Sandy _____ finish her book, but she read the _____

   story anyway.

6. The Marche Company hasn't hired a shipping clerk because they haven't found

   the _____ person for the job.

7. I do different exercises every day. My friends also _____ _____

   exercises.

Lesson 124

Part A

s or es   s or es

1. study + _____ = _____   5. cry + _____ = _____

2. story + _____ = _____   6. joy + _____ = _____

3. play + _____ = _____   7. city + _____ = _____

4. glory + _____ = _____   8. fly + _____ = _____

Part B

1. _____

2. _____

Part C

1. _____   4. _____

2. _____   5. _____

3. _____   6. _____

Part D

listen	proclaim	reason	style
largest	sleepy	search	picture
school	pitiful	question	straight

Part E

Make 11 real words from the morphographs in the box.

hot	ly	sturdy	er	mad	nasty	est

1. _____   7. _____

2. _____   8. _____

3. _____   9. _____

4. _____   10. _____

5. _____   11. _____

6. _____

Lesson 126

Part A

1. show   2. water   3. know   4. law   5. whether   6. blow

Part B

         s or **es**   **s** or **es**

1. copy + _____ = _____   5. city + _____ = _____

2. spray + _____ = _____   6. worry + _____ = _____

3. fly   + _____ = _____   7. study + _____ = _____

4. boy   + _____ = _____   8. story + _____ = _____

Part C

Write the contractions for the words in the first column.

1. were not = _____   5. let us   = _____

2. have not = _____   6. are not   = _____

3. you will = _____   7. would not = _____

4. they had = _____   8. does not = _____

Part D

Fill in the blanks to show the morphographs in each word.

1. _____ + _____ = relate

2. _____ + _____ + _____ = relative

3. _____ + _____ + _____ = actively

4. _____ + _____ + _____ = expressive

5. _____ + _____ + _____ = inactive

6. _____ + _____ = moving

7. _____ + _____ + _____ = removal

8. _____ + _____ = proverb

9. _____ + _____ = react

10. _____ + _____ + _____ = reaction

Lesson 127

Part A

1. _____

2. _____

Part B

1. _____   4. _____

2. _____   5. _____

3. _____   6. _____

Part C

Part D

Write **s** or **es** in the second column. Then add the morphographs together.

	s or **es**				**s** or **es**	
1. tax	+ _____	= _____		6. copy	+ _____	= _____
2. study	+ _____	= _____		7. thought	+ _____	= _____
3. play	+ _____	= _____		8. worry	+ _____	= _____
4. brush	+ _____	= _____		9. spray	+ _____	= _____
5. reason	+ _____	= _____		10. baby	+ _____	= _____

Lesson 128

Part A

1. _____   4. _____

2. _____   5. _____

3. _____   6. _____

Part B

Circle each short word that ends **cvc.**

1. reason   4. win   7. form   10. cover

2. stop   5. snap   8. fit   11. spin

3. grow   6. boy   9. stay   12. big

Part C

Add the morphographs together.

1. please + ing = _____   6. re + late + ive = _____

2. worry + es   = _____   7. story + es   = _____

3. neat + ness = _____   8. fit + ing   = _____

4. study + ed   = _____   9. pity + ful   = _____

5. sad + ness   = _____   10. wrap + er   = _____

Part D

Figure out the rules and write them.

1. **c** in a short word when . . . morphograph begins with **v** . . . the word ends . . . Double the final . . . **cvc** and the next

   _____

   _____

2. a word when the word ends with . . . next morphograph begins with anything, except **i** . . . a consonant-and-**y** and the . . . Change the **y** to **i** in

   _____

   _____

Lesson 129

Part A

1. _____
2. _____
3. _____
4. _____

5. _____
6. _____
7. _____

Part B

1. _____
2. _____
3. _____

4. _____
5. _____
6. _____

Part C

Make 11 real words from the morphographs in the box.

less	thought	ness	hope	ly	ful

1. _____
2. _____
3. _____
4. _____
5. _____
6. _____

7. _____
8. _____
9. _____
10. _____
11. _____

Part D

Complete each sentence correctly with one of these words:

write   feat   their   hole   whole   vary   right   threw

1. The detective thinks that she is not telling the _____ truth.

2. Jan swam across the raging river, which was a brave _____ .

3. I used to print my name, but now I _____ it.

4. The restaurants on Miller Street are popular because they _____ their menu daily.

5. A strongman at the circus performed a different _____ of strength during every show.

6. The students checked _____ answers.

    Every student got every answer _____ .

7. We _____ beanbags through a _____ in the wall.

Lesson 130

Part A

1. _____   4. _____

2. _____   5. _____

3. _____   6. _____

Part B

1. _____

2. _____

3. _____

4. _____

Part C

Write the contractions for the words in the first column.

1. what is   = _____

2. would not = _____

3. can not   = _____

4. they have = _____

5. he will   = _____

6. are not   = _____

7. it is   = _____

8. they are = _____

Part D

Add the morphographs together.

1. bench + es = _____

2. try + es   = _____

3. nice + ly   = _____

4. early + er   = _____

5. copy + es   = _____

6. happy + ness = _____

7. worry + ed   = _____

8. stay + s   = _____

Lesson 131

Part A

1. _____

2. _____

3. _____

4. _____

5. _____

6. _____

Part B

1. _____

2. _____

158

Part C

These words are in the puzzle.
Circle 7 or more of the words

station   headed   stress

business   form   ruin

night   fires   meet

depart   equal   farms

```
m h s s f f f f
m e e t t o i a
d e p a r t r r
r q t t d e e m
b u s i n e s s
h a i o s s d s
s l i n i g h t
```

Part D

Fill in the blanks to show the morphographs in each word.

1. _____ + _____ = request

2. _____ + _____ = question

3. _____ + _____ = conquest

4. _____ + _____ = varied

5. _____ + _____ = various

6. _____ + _____ = stepped

7. _____ + _____ = lately

8. _____ + _____ + _____ = relation

Lesson 132

Part A

1. _____

2. _____

Part B

1. _____   4. _____

2. _____   5. _____

3. _____   6. _____

Part C

Part D

Add the morphographs together.

1. danger + ous   = _____

2. worth + y + ness   = _____

3. quest + ion + able = _____

4. straight + en + ing = _____

5. probe + ing   = _____

6. like + ly + ness   = _____

7. force + ful + ly   = _____

8. note + ion   = _____

9. carry + age   = _____

10. city + es   = _____

11. try + al   = _____

12. con + tract + ion = _____

Lesson 133

Part A

1. _____   4. _____

2. _____   5. _____

3. _____   6. _____

Part B

1. _____ + _____ = _____

2. _____ + _____ = _____

3. _____ + _____ = _____

4. _____ + _____ = _____

5. _____ + _____ = _____

6. _____ + _____ = _____

Part C

Draw a line from each word to its clue.

would •   • in that place

there •   • My friends save _____ money.

here •   • We had a _____ good lunch.

hear •   • contraction of **they are**

very •   • How _____ you like a surprise?

plain •   • We expect better _____ tomorrow.

they're •   • Please speak louder. I can't _____ you.

their •   • in this place

weather •   • part of something

piece •   • ordinary

Lesson 134

Part A

1. _____   4. _____

2. _____   5. _____

3. _____   6. _____

Part B

1. _____ + _____ = _____

2. _____ + _____ = _____

3. _____ + _____ = _____

4. _____ + _____ = _____

5. _____ + _____ = _____

6. _____ + _____ = _____

Part C

Part D

Figure out the rules and write them.

1. with anything, except **i** . . . the next morphograph begins . . . **i** in a word when the . . . Change the **y** to . . . word ends consonant-and-**y** and

_____

_____

2. with **v** . . . morphograph begins . . . word when the next . . . **e** from a . . . Drop the

_____

_____

Lesson 136

Part A

1. _____

2. _____

3. _____

4. _____

Part B

Complete each sentence correctly with one of these words:

their   witch   through   threw   whether   eight   loan   tale

1. I had _____ good reasons for staying home.

2. They wanted to _____ me some money, but _____ pockets were empty.

3. We have to decide _____ or not we will go.

4. Mr. Samuels told us a _____ about a _____ who could turn stone into gold.

5. We saw him _____ the window.

6. The girls _____ a few pebbles into the river.

7. Ivan and Roberta started _____ own business.

Part C

Add the morphographs together.

1. try + al = _____

2. con + tract + ion = _____

3. re + late + ive + ly = _____

4. city + es = _____

5. un + like + ly + ness = _____

6. ex + press + ion = _____

7. beauty + ful + ly = _____

8. noise + y + ness = _____

9. re + cent + ly = _____

10. in + cure + able = _____

11. un + ex + plain + ed = _____

12. re + late + ion = _____

Lesson 137

Part A

1. _____

2. _____

3. _____

4. _____

Part B

1. _____   4. _____

2. _____   5. _____

3. _____   6. _____

Part C

_____

_____

_____

_____

_____

Part D

Cross out the misspelled words in these sentences.
Then write the words correctly above the crossed-out words.

I could'nt here the teecher.

The whether has been beautyful this weck.

How many storys will the author right?

Lesson 138

Part A

1. _____ + _____ = _____

2. _____ + _____ = _____

3. _____ + _____ = _____

4. _____ + _____ = _____

5. _____ + _____ = _____

6. _____ + _____ = _____

Part B

1. _____

2. _____

Part C

Part D

Write **s** or **es** in the second column.
Then add the morphographs together.

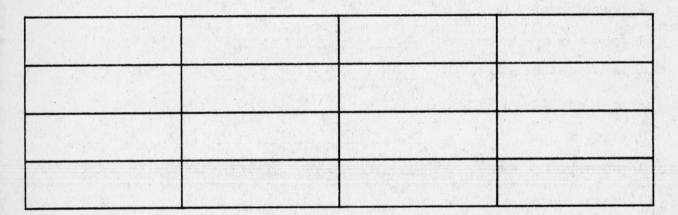

	s or es			s or es
1. scratch + _____ = _____		5. fly + _____ = _____		
2. copy + _____ = _____		6. hurry + _____ = _____		
3. wash + _____ = _____		7. dress + _____ = _____		
4. boy + _____ = _____		8. plan + _____ = _____		

Lesson 139

Part A

1. _____

2. _____

Part B

1. _____   3. _____

2. _____   4. _____

Part C

Add the morphographs together.

1. un + in + form + ed   = _____

2. rate + ion   = _____

3. re + strict + ed   = _____

4. peace + ful + ly   = _____

5. fury + ous   = _____

6. re + late + ive + ly   = _____

7. in + act + ive   = _____

8. study + ous   = _____

9. pro + port + ion   = _____

10. create + ive   = _____

Part D

Fill in the blanks to show the morphographs in each word.

1. _____ + _____ = snapping

2. _____ + _____ = rightful

3. _____ + _____ + _____ = depression

4. _____ + _____ + _____ = actively

5. _____ + _____ = various

6. _____ + _____ + _____ = proclaimed

MEANINGS OF PREFIXES AND SUFFIXES

Morphograph	Lesson	Meanings	Examples
-able	33	(able to be)	stretchable, washable, readable
-al	59	(related to, like)	formal, trial, rental
-age	57	(that which is, state)	package, usage, marriage
con-	79	(with, together; really)	conform, contest, condense
de-	53	(away from, down; negative)	deport, deform, describe
-ed	36	(in the past; quality)	stepped, cried, wooded
-en	56	(make; in the past; quality of)	loosen, bitten, proven
-er	41	(more; one who, that which)	easier, lighter, trapper
-es	77	(more than one; a verb marker for he, she or it)	matches, boxes, carries
-est	24	(the most)	lightest, happiest, friendliest
ex-	105	(out, away)	export, expose, exclude
-ful	54	(full of)	careful, forgetful, beautiful
in-	78	(in, into; not; really)	intake, incurable, invaluable
-ing	21	(when you do something; quality, state)	spending, moving, stopping
-ion	126	(state, quality, act)	action, taxation, repression
-ish	60	(like, related to; make)	babyish, selfish, finish
-ive	123	(one who, quality of)	relative, expressive, active
-less	26	(without)	painless, useless, restless
-ly	42	(how something is)	equally, basically, motherly
-ment	95	(that which is; quality, act)	placement, requirement, apartment
mis-	27	(wrong)	misspell, mistrial, misprint
-ness	32	(that which is; state, quality)	thickness, uselessness, thoughtfulness
-ous	131	(having the quality of)	famous, furious, joyous
pre-	39	(before)	preview, preclude, prepay
pro-	121	(before; forward)	proclaim, provision, prolong
re-	21	(again, back, really)	rerun, return, replace
-s	75	(more than one; a verb marker for he, she or it)	parks, friends, designs
un-	23	(not; reversal of)	unhappy, unusual, untie
-y	69	(having the quality of; in the manner of; small)	shiny, activity, doggy

SPELLING RULES AND PRINCIPLES

Lesson 6	**C-k Rule**	"If a word ends in **-ack, -eck, -ick, -ock,** or **-uck,** the last part is spelled with **c-k.**"
Lesson 11	**D-g-e Rule**	"If a word ends in **-adge, edge, -idge, -odge,** or **-udge,** the last part is spelled with **d-g-e.**"
Lesson 36	**T-c-h Rule**	"If a word ends in **-atch, -etch, -itch,** or **-otch,** the last part is spelled with **t-c-h.**"
Lesson 37	**Final E Rule**	"When a word ends in **e** and you add a morphograph that begins with a vowel letter, drop the **e.**"
Lesson 53	**Doubling Rule**	"When a short word ends **cvc** and the next morphograph begins with a **v,** double the final **c.**"
Lesson 61	**Vowel-Consonant**	"**Y** at the end of a morphograph is a vowel letter."
Lesson 75	**Y to I Rule**	"Change the **y** to **i** when a word ends with a consonant-and-**y,** and the next morphograph begins with anything, except **i.**"
Lesson 77	**Plural-Variation**	"If a word ends in **s, sh,** or **ch,** you add **es** to make the plural word."
Lesson 81	**Plural-Variation**	"If a word ends in **s, sh, ch,** or **x,** you add **es** to make the plural word. The letter **x** acts like two consonant letters."
Lesson 99	**Contractions**	"A contraction is made from two words, and a contraction has a part missing. We show that the part is missing with an apostrophe."
Lesson 121	**Plural Variation**	"If a word ends with a consonant-and-**y,** you add **es** to make the plural word."
Lesson 126	**Vowel-Consonant**	"**W** at the end of a morphograph is a vowel letter."

above
action
active
actively
answer
aren't
arms
ask
athlete
athletes
author
babies
babyish
back
badge
baker
bare
bared
barely
bareness
barer
barest
baring
barred
beautiful
beautifully
beauty
been
beetle
before
believable
believe
bench
benches
best
better
big
bigger
biggest
bike
bite
biting
black
blackest
blackness
blame
blameless
bliss
blissful
bloomed
blow
blowing
blue
bluest
boat
boats

bold
boldness
book
books
born
boss
bound
boundless
box
boxes
boxing
boy
boyish
boyishness
boys
brain
break
breakable
breathe
brick
bride
bridge
brief
briefest
briefly
brightest
brightness
broom
brown
brownest
brownish
brush
brushes
brushing
budge
build
building
bush
bushes
busiest
business
busy
cage
can't
care
cared
careful
carefully
careless
carelessly
caring
carriage
carried
carrier
carries
carry

carrying
catch
catched
catcher
catches
caught
cause
chain
chalk
change
changeless
changes
changing
charge
charm
charming
cheap
cheaper
cheapest
cheaply
chief
chiefly
child
childish
childishly
childishness
children
chill
chiming
choice
choicest
choke
choking
cities
city
civil
civilly
claim
claims
clapping
clashes
class
classes
clock
close
clothes
cloud
cloudiness
cloudless
clouds
cloudy
coat
coil
coin
cold
colder

coldest
coldness
come
coming
confine
confined
confinement
confining
confirmed
conform
conformed
conforming
confront
confronted
confuse
confusing
conquest
consent
conserve
consign
consignment
constrict
contacted
contest
context
contract
contracted
contraction
cool
coolest
cope
copied
copies
copy
copying
cork
could
couldn't
count
counting
cover
crash
crashes
creative
cried
crier
cries
crying
cube
curable
cure
cured
curing
danger
dangerous
darkness

date
deal
dealer
dealing
deck
decoded
defacing
defaulted
defeat
defeated
define
defined
defining
deform
degrade
degrading
delight
delighted
delightful
delighting
denial
denied
dented
deny
denying
depart
departed
department
deport
depress
depressed
depressing
depression
deserve
deserved
deserving
design
designed
designer
desk
desks
detract
devalue
didn't
different
dined
diner
dining
dishes
ditch
dodge
doesn't
dog
done
dosage
drain

drainage
dress
dresses
dressing
dressy
dried
dripless
dripped
dripping
drive
driving
drop
dropped
dropper
dropping
drying
duck
dull
earlier
earliest
early
ease
easily
easy
edge
eight
else
endless
endlessly
ends
enough
equal
equally
error
especially
even
every
everyone
exchange
exchanging
exciting
exclaim
explained
export
exported
express
expression
expressive
face
faced
facing
facts
fail
failing
fame
fancied

fancier	foolishly	gracefully	homeless	kindness	long
fanciest	forceful	grade	hope	kite	look
fanciful	forcefully	grader	hoped	know	lost
fancy	fork	grading	hopeful	lace	loud
fancying	form	grand	hopefully	lake	loudest
farm	formal	grandest	hopefulness	landed	loudly
farmer	formally	grandly	hopeless	large	lovable
farms	formed	grape	hopelessly	largely	love
fatal	former	great	hopelessness	larger	low
fatally	formless	greatest	hoping	largest	lower
fate	forms	greatly	hot	late	luck
fault	found	greatness	hotly	lately	lucky
faultless	fox	green	hotter	latest	lunch
feat	foxes	greenest	hottest	leader	lunches
feel	frame	greenness	house	leakage	mad
feet	freshen	grief	huge	leash	madden
fence	freshest	gripping	human	leave	madder
fight	friend	ground	humanness	ledge	maddest
fighter	friendless	grounded	hurried	left	made
fill	friendliest	grow	hurries	length	madly
final	friendliness	growing	hurry	lengthen	madness
finally	friendly	happiest	hurrying	lengthening	main
fine	friends	happily	I'll	lengthy	mainly
fined	fright	happiness	inactive	let's	make
finely	fringe	happy	income	life	many
fineness	from	hard	incurable	lifeless	mask
finer	front	harm	inflaming	light	match
finest	fudge	harmlessly	inform	lighten	matches
fining	furious	hasn't	informal	lighter	meat
finish	fury	hate	informed	lightest	meet
finished	fuse	have	informer	lighting	mess
fire	fuss	haven't	inhuman	lightly	messes
fired	fussy	he'll	instated	lights	mighty
fires	gain	he's	instilled	likable	milk
firing	game	headed	insure	like	misjudge
first	gave	hear	intended	liked	misjudged
fish	girlishness	heard	invaluable	likeliest	mismatched
fishing	given	heaviest	investment	likeliness	misplace
fit	glass	heavy	isn't	likely	misplaced
fitness	glasses	hedge	it's	liken	misprinted
fitting	global	helped	I've	likeness	misquoted
flatten	globe	helper	joint	likes	misshapen
flattest	glories	helpful	jointly	liking	misspell
flier	glorious	helpless	joke	listen	misspelling
flies	glory	helplessly	joker	listening	misstep
flight	goat	helplessness	joking	little	mistake
float	goats	herb	joyful	load	mistaken
floating	going	here	joyfully	loan	misuse
flow	gold	hide	joys	lock	misused
flower	golden	hire	judge	locker	moss
flowers	good	hired	judged	lodge	most
fluid	goodness	hiring	judging	lone	mothering
fly	govern	hit	keep	loneliest	motor
flying	government	hold	kept	loneliness	motoring
fold	grace	hole	kick	lonely	motors
foolish	graceful	home	kindest	loneness	movable

move	paints	points	quietly	relatively	ride
moved	park	poison	quietness	remain	ridge
movement	parked	poisoning	quite	remaining	right
mover	part	poisonous	quiz	remark	rightful
moving	passes	poke	quotable	remarkable	rightfully
nail	passive	porch	quote	removal	ripe
nails	past	port	race	remove	ripeness
name	patch	portable	races	removed	ripest
nameless	patches	predated	racing	removing	rise
namely	pause	prejudge	rage	renamed	risen
nastier	payment	preplan	raging	rental	rising
nastiest	peace	preplanned	rail	rented	robe
nastily	peaceful	preschool	rain	renter	rock
neat	peacefully	presented	rainy	renting	room
neatly	people	preserve	rake	repack	rooms
neatness	person	preserved	rate	repacked	rope
neck	personable	preserving	ration	repacking	rough
need	personally	preshrunk	reach	repay	rougher
needlessly	pick	press	reaches	replace	roughest
nerve	picking	presses	react	replaced	roughness
nervous	picture	pressing	reacting	replacement	round
new	pictures	preview	reaction	replacing	rowboats
nice	piece	previewed	read	report	ruin
nicely	pinch	previewing	real	reported	ruined
nicer	pinches	prewrap	really	reporter	run
nicest	pine	prime	reason	reporting	runner
niece	pipe	print	reasonable	repression	running
night	pitch	probing	reasons	request	sack
nightly	pitied	proclaim	rebuild	requesting	sad
nights	pitiful	proclaimed	rebuilding	research	sadden
noise	pity	profile	recently	researching	saddening
noisiness	pitying	profound	recoiled	reserve	sadder
noisy	place	profoundly	recover	reserved	saddest
none	plain	prolong	redefine	reserving	sadly
normal	plan	prolonged	redefined	resign	sadness
normally	planned	proportion	redefining	resigned	safe
notable	planner	proud	redesign	resort	safely
notch	planners	proudly	refill	resorted	safest
note	planning	prove	refillable	resource	sail
noted	plans	proven	refine	resourceful	sailboat
noting	plant	proverb	refined	rest	sailboats
notion	plants	prowl	refinement	rested	sailing
nudge	plate	pure	refining	restful	sale
nudging	play	pureness	reform	restfully	sank
often	played	purest	reformed	resting	saw
old	player	put	refresh	restless	scary
other	playful	putting	refreshing	restlessly	school
our	playfully	quest	refreshment	restlessness	schools
out	playing	question	refusal	restore	scope
pack	plays	questionable	regained	restricted	scratch
package	please	questions	rehiring	rethinking	scratched
packaging	pleasing	quick	reinstate	retract	scratches
page	pledge	quickest	relate	review	search
painful	point	quickly	related	reviewed	searched
paint	pointless	quiet	relation	reviewer	searching
painter	pointlessness	quietest	relative	rewrite	second

see	slightest	starless	sturdiness	thoughtful	unbreakable
serve	slightly	starred	sturdy	thoughtfully	unchanging
served	slipped	starring	style	thoughtfulness	uncivil
server	slipping	stars	stylish	thoughtless	uncivilly
serving	slope	started	stylishly	thoughtlessly	unclaimed
several	slowly	state	sudden	thoughtlessness	unclear
shake	smell	stately	suddenly	thoughts	unconfirmed
shaken	smile	statement	sure	three	uncovered
shame	smiling	station	surprise	threw	uncurable
shameless	smoke	stay	surprised	throat	undefeated
shape	smoked	stayed	swim	through	undeserving
shaping	smokeless	stays	swimmer	throw	undone
she'll	smoker	step	swimmers	time	undrinkable
she's	snail	stepped	swimming	timed	unequal
shine	snake	stepping	switch	timeless	unequally
shining	snapping	stitch	tack	timer	unexplained
shiny	snugly	stitches	tail	times	unfilling
ship	snugness	stone	tails	tires	unfolding
shipment	soap	stood	take	to	unhappy
shock	soil	stop	taken	together	uninformed
shoes	sold	stopped	taking	told	unkindest
shoot	some	stopping	tale	took	unkindness
shop	sort	storage	talk	touch	unlikable
shopped	sound	store	talked	touched	unlike
shopper	soundly	stories	talker	touching	unlikeliness
shopping	soundness	storing	tame	tough	unlikely
shops	sounds	story	tape	toughest	unlock
shore	source	straight	tax	toughness	unlocking
short	south	straighten	taxes	town	unlucky
shortest	space	straightening	teach	toy	unmask
shortly	speak	straightest	teacher	toys	unmistakable
should	speaker	strained	tell	trace	unmoved
shouldn't	speaks	strange	test	tracing	unnerved
shove	speech	strangely	text	track	unpacked
show	speeches	stranger	than	tract	unpacking
shrunk	speechless	strangest	thank	trail	unplanned
sick	speediest	street	that	trailer	unpreserved
side	spell	strength	that's	trapped	unproven
sign	speller	strengthen	their	trapper	unquotable
signal	spelling	strengthening	them	trial	unreachable
signs	spend	stress	then	trick	unreadable
silk	spending	stretch	there	tricky	unrecoverable
since	spinning	stretchable	these	tried	unrefined
sing	spite	stretched	they	tries	unrefreshing
sizable	spot	stretcher	they'd	trip	unrelated
size	spotless	stretches	they'll	tripped	unreserved
skate	spotted	stretching	they're	trips	unripened
sketch	spotty	stuck	they've	truck	unshaken
sketching	sprain	studied	thick	trust	unsnapped
skidded	spray	studies	thickness	try	unsold
skill	sprayed	studious	thief	trying	unsound
skillfully	sprays	study	think	turn	unsoundest
skipping	stage	studying	thinking	twice	unsoundness
slammed	staging	sturdier	this	type	unstuck
sleepy	stain	sturdiest	those	unable	unsturdy
slice	star	sturdily	thought	unbelievable	unthinkable

unthinking	valuing	washable	where	witch	worthless
untrusting	varied	washes	whether	witches	worthy
untyped	various	washing	which	with	would
unusable	vary	wasn't	while	wonder	wouldn't
unused	verb	watch	white	wondered	wrap
unvaried	verbally	watched	whiter	wonderful	wrapped
unworkable	very	watches	whitest	wonderfully	wrapper
unwrap	view	watching	who	wondering	wrapping
usable	vine	water	whole	wood	wreck
usage	voice	watered	whose	work	wreckage
used	voltage	watering	wide	workable	write
useful	vote	we'll	widely	working	writing
usefully	wage	we're	widen	world	wrong
useless	wake	we've	wideness	worldly	wrote
uselessly	wander	weaken	widening	worried	yardage
uselessness	wandered	weather	widest	worrier	yellow
user	wandering	weed	win	worries	you'll
using	want	were	winner	worry	you're
valuable	wanted	weren't	winners	worrying	you've
value	was	what	winning	worth	your
valueless	wash	what's	wishes	worthiness	